THE ROYAL MARINES COMMANDOS
FITNESS & SURVIVAL SKILLS
John Watney

'. . . it is a tough course — one of the toughest of its kind in the world. After all we are in the business of making commandos and there is no place for the inadequate or the half hearted.'
(Civilian into Serviceman . . . Serviceman into Commando, issued by the Royal Marines.)

The Author

John Watney served in the Army throughout World War II, in the Derbyshire Yeomanry before being seconded to the Polish Army and later the Belgian Army. He saw action in North Africa and France. His interest in the work and methods of the Royal Marines has taken him on many exercises with them, in training grounds as varied as the Arctic and the Mediterranean.

D1586120

THE
ROYAL MARINES
COMMANDOS
Fitness & Survival Skills

JOHN WATNEY

HIPPOCRENE
BOOKS, INC.

DAVID & CHARLES
Newton Abbot   London
HIPPOCRENE BOOKS INC.
New York

Photographs on pages 8, 9, 75, 84 and 102 and all line illustrations reproduced courtesy of Commando Forces.
All other photographs taken by the author.

Jacket photographs taken by the author except for the bottom right-hand picture on the back of the jacket, reproduced courtesy of Commando Forces.

The 5BX exercises are from *Physical Fitness* by the Royal Canadian Air Force (Penguin Books, 1964), Crown Copyright by the Queen's Printer, Canada.

British Library Cataloguing in Publication Data

Watney John
  The Royal Marine commandos fitness and survival skills.
  1. Physical fitness   2. Wilderness survival
  3. Outdoor life—Safety measures
  I. Title
  613.7   RA781

ISBN 0–7153–8716–2 (hbk)
      0–7153–9115–1 (pbk)

First published 1987
Paperback edition June 1988
Reprinted August 1988
Reprinted 1989

Printed in Great Britain
by Redwood Burn Ltd, Trowbridge Wilts
for David & Charles Publishers plc
Brunel House   Newton Abbot   Devon

Published in the United States of America
by Hippocrene Books Inc
171 Madison Avenue, New York, NY 10016
ISBN 0–87052–715–0

CONTENTS

INTRODUCTION

The Royal Marines recruit young men between the ages of 17 and 28 from a wide variety of backgrounds, very few of whom will have had any experience of outdoor or adventurous pursuits. They are not chosen for exceptional physique (although they are all reasonably fit by civilian standards but are at the bottom of the tree by Royal Marine standards). In thirty weeks of recruit training they will develop muscles where there were none, and achieve things they had never dreamt they would ever be able to do. At the end of that time, having passed some of the toughest physical tests ever devised, they are given their green berets and called Commandos. It is a remarkable achievement in the time; even more remarkable is the fact that the fitness and endurance training methods have hardly changed since they were devised towards the end of World War II. That they work was again proved during the Falklands battle where many of the Royal Marines were only a few weeks out of recruit training.

Officially, everything done in the Royal Marines is designed to develop purposeful military skills in men who are physically and mentally prepared for war. Having said that, the reality is that although everything that a Marine does has a military context, most of it can be described equally in civilian language as advanced outdoor activities and adventure sports. Leave aside the camouflage clothing and the weapons — and most of the time they do just that — and what we see are superbly fit and well taught men doing backpacking, crosscountry and hill walking, orienteering and navigating, camping and field crafts, rock, snow and ice climbing, crosscountry skiing, canoeing, sub-aqua diving and parachuting. Both serving and ex-Commandos are much in demand as members and leaders of national and international expeditions to all parts of the world,

Trained Commandos going ashore from a landing craft

and as instructors at climbing and outdoor pursuits centres. It must therefore follow that much can be gleaned from their continuing experience over the years and their training methods, which can usefully be applied to many forms of civilian outdoor activities and adventure particularly by novices—which is what every Marine recruit is when he joins.

This book is based on the training manuals used by the Royal Marines Commandos, the knowledge and experience passed on by instructors and training teams, and personal observation of them at work. However, the reader must understand that a Royal Marines Commando learns his fitness and survival skills over a long period and under the supervision of expert instructors. The individual civilian would be foolhardy to try to emulate those commando skills unless or until he has achieved a well above average standard of fitness. And even then he will need to pace himself very carefully. Potentially hazardous activities should only be attempted in the company of responsible and experienced companions and, in certain instances, only with competent safety and rescue back-up.

CHAPTER 1

FROM CIVILIAN TO COMMANDO

At the beginning of his training a recruit is given a light PT programme, which gradually progresses, allowing any weaker member a chance to build up for the very demanding Commando tests that will face him in the latter stages. The first PT periods, known as Initial Military Fitness Training, consist of two tables of Swedish PT in the gymnasium that provide a good foundation, tone the body and are progressively graded. Still in the gym the recruit then adds 'military skills' to his PT

New recruits doing rope work in the gym

Recruit on the Tarzan course

work with gate vaults, jumping and landing techniques, rope climbing and general body co-ordination exercises. After that he moves out into the open and starts working on elements of the assault course, where he learns to get his body back onto a tightrope after rolling under it, is put on a high obstacle course to gain confidence, and does more rope climbing. He also learns and practises the fireman's lift against the day when he needs to carry an injured man to safety.

By this time he is wearing uniform and boots instead of gym kit, has developed and strengthened good cardiovascular fitness and is ready to start his battle fitness training when he is introduced to the whole assault course. This he must be able to complete in 5 minutes wearing full fighting order and carrying his rifle, a total weight of 18 to 20kg (40 to 45lb). Humping the same load he must also carry a man and all his equipment 183m (200yds) in under 90 seconds followed by a full regain back onto a rope. Also wearing full fighting order he has to jump from the 3m (10ft) board into a swimming pool, swim

50m (55yds), come back to the side, take off his equipment and hand it up to an instructor without touching the side of the pool, and then stay afloat treading water for any time left of his allotted 3 minutes.

During the weeks of this strenuous physical training he will be developing endurance, stamina and field crafts on day and night exercises, crosscountry marches, harsh survival on Dartmoor, cliff scaling and absciling, not to mention a fair amount of tiring parade ground drill. In camp he never walks about; he always quick marches. In his twenty-fourth week he is introduced to the Tarzan course, so beloved of press and TV cameramen, where high above the ground he will learn all the methods of crossing gaps known to the Royal Marines. He must progress to a degree of expertise where he can complete that course in 5 minutes, and then do the combined assault and Tarzan courses in 12 minutes. If anything is going to make a man wish Commando training was just a bad dream from which he could wake himself, it is the aptly named endurance course on Woodbury Common in winter. It is run through

Recruit entering submerged tunnel on the Endurance course

bog, mud, obstacles, tunnels (even a submerged sewage pipe has to be negotiated), and all in fighting order with the added encumbrance of a rifle. This course is done in groups of three or four to test teamwork. On the run back to camp there is a cartoon poster nailed to a tree; it shows a weary Royal Marines recruit bent double and sweating and it bears the legend: 'It is only pain, 500 metres to go.' Even back in camp at the end of those last agonising 500 metres there is no rest. To pass the course each recruit must show that he is still able to fight and so, without time to get his breath back, he must fire five rounds with his still wet and slimy rifle and hit the target.

After all these progressive build-ups and tests, including a 14.5km (9 mile) speed march to be completed in 90 minutes he is ready, hopefully, for the ultimate test—the 30-miler. Again, in full fighting order, carrying rifle and ammunition, he must navigate and cross 48km (30 miles) of the roughest and most demanding terrain of Dartmoor in under 8 hours; for young officers it is 7 hours. Once he has completed this final test he is no longer a recruit; he is given his green beret and is called a Royal Marines commando.

CHAPTER 2

BREAKING THE MOULD

If you get out of breath running for a bus, walking up Helvellyn will be sheer agony. The successful enjoyment of any strenuous outdoor activity requires a standard of physical fitness above the average, and for most people achieving that means a serious decision to train and to break any bad habits. In the Commandos the aims of military fitness training are laid down as:

1 Muscular strength, muscular endurance, flexibility, good posture and neuromuscular co-ordination, all of which are common to every form of sport and athletics.

2 The physical skills necessary in combat, which include fast movement in confined spaces, balance and overcoming fear of heights, vaulting and jumping and landing correctly, falling safely, rope climbing, negotiation of obstacles both natural and man-made, an economic running style and swimming. The word 'combat' is easily changed to 'adventure sports'.

3 Physical character covering a healthy lifestyle, self-confidence, will-power, self-discipline, quick reaction and speed, mental endurance, a fighting spirit and the will to win. Are those not qualities we would all like to have, even the last two, in their sporting context?

Those are the aims to be attained within an ideal training environment and with all facilities available, as they are at the Commando Training Centre. However, even in less than ideal conditions, it is still possible to reach a high standard of physical fitness and maintain it, if given the will to do so. But it requires a determined effort and personal commitment to reach and maintain a healthy lifestyle in the soft options' society in which we live, with physical activity engineered out of most forms of work. The resulting inactivity causes unfitness, which can lead to hypertension, chronic fatigue, poor musculature, lack of flexibility, lower back pain, obesity, heart disease and, with an insiduous degeneration of the body, low resistance to infection and disease and premature ageing. Surely such a gloomy catalogue of afflictions should be enough to inspire anybody to make that determined effort to achieve a healthy lifestyle for its own sake, regardless of any adventurous ambitions.

If you are not in a group PT programme you can design a personal one to suit your time and facilities, which should aim to be enjoyable so that it becomes part of your lifestyle. The notes that follow are intended to provide some basic knowledge of the essential components of physical fitness and various types of exercises and their purpose so that you can devise a meaningful programme.

1 *Muscular strength* is the maximum single effort of force that can be exerted against a resistance. Strength was at one time thought to be the main sign of physical fitness, but more recently the emphasis has been on the functional capacity of the individual to supply energy to working muscles. Often neglected in the past was upper body strength, eg the ability to pull one's body weight up above shoulder height and over obstacles especially with the added weight of any equipment being carried — a most important factor in climbing and crosscountry skiing. A low level of muscular strength has the side effects of making it difficult both to maintain a good upright posture and to move with economy of effort.

2 *Muscular endurance* is the ability of muscles to contract repeatedly and remain contracted for a long time before fatigue sets in. Endurance specific to each muscle group needs to be developed separately. The limiting factor is mostly within the muscle itself.

3 *Cardiovascular endurance* is simply the maximum amount of physical work that an individual can sustain over an extended

14

period. This largely depends on the body's ability to supply oxygen to the muscles doing the work. The heart, circulatory and respiratory systems all need to be functioning efficiently if a good level of cardiovascular endurance is to be maintained. It is certainly the most important aspect of physical fitness.

4 *Flexibility* means the ability of joints to articulate through the full range of their movements. Loss of flexibility is common among elderly people, but a young inactive person will be less flexible than an active one. With inactivity muscles settle into a permanent state of contraction and will need a lot of stretching exercises to restore their flexibility.

A good work programme will cater for those four components, but do not expect too much too soon. There is no short cut to physical fitness, and initially it will take from ten to twelve weeks of serious work to establish a fitness base; thereafter there must be a long term, if not a lifetime, commitment to maintain it. The best combination of exercise is aerobic work — by which the amount of air taken in, the amount of blood circulated by the heart and the amount of oxygen carried to the muscles are all enhanced — and isotonic training, which develops a full range of movement and progressively strengthens the muscles. Regularity is more important than the amount of exercise that is done, and a programme can be called regular when it is carried out three to four times a week. But if very strenuous exercise is done on several consecutive days the glycogen stored in the liver and muscles as a reserve of energy will be depleted, therefore rest periods must be included in any programme.

The work should be progressive with a balanced co-ordination of all the muscle groups. There is no benefit in going on to harder exercises until the simpler ones can be done easily. There will be progressive improvement only if the body is given a challenge by being worked beyond its normal capacity, but not to the point of exhaustion; this is called 'overload'. It takes motivation to sustain a physical fitness programme and many fall by the wayside through boredom. It is particularly hard to keep up enthusiasm on your own, so try and work together with someone else or in a group as often as possible and introduce variety into exercises, and into the location and terrain. It is accepted that a minimum of three workouts a week are needed to develop cardiovascular fitness. Ground is quickly lost when training is stopped, but if strength and endurance have been acquired over a long period they will survive occasional breaks.

To achieve improvement in condition your pulse rate must hit 70 to 85 per cent of its maximum rate (not its resting rate), which can be estimated by subtracting your age from the figure 220. Below 60 per cent of your maximum heart rate you are wasting your time. A good target guide for training effect is between 150 and 180 beats per minute. The average person should aim to exercise hard for between 20 and 30 minutes each session. Many will not at first be able to cope with high intensity work, so they should work for longer, say for 45 minutes, at a lower intensity of around 130 heart beats per minute. To those times must be added 10 minutes for preliminary warm-up and 10 minutes for cooling down. In addition to PT exercises there are other activities of an aerobic type (demanding big oxygen consumption and using large muscle groups), at least one of which should be undertaken on a regular basis. Among the best are crosscountry running, jogging, swimming, basketball and cycling.

Before embarking on an intensive programme you should have a medical examination if you have not had one in the past year, or if you are over 30 years of age, or are overweight, or if you have a history of high blood pressure or heart trouble. From that you will want to know your present level of physical fitness. Before going into a physical training programme it is important to establish your present level of fitness. There is a Personal Fitness Test which is designed to be done with the minimal equipment and organisation which, when completed, will give a very good indication of your standard of fitness. It can be carried out as a self-test.

The test is in two parts:

1 — Muscular strength and endurance.
2 — Cardiovascular endurance.

The only equipment needed is a pull-up bar (such as a

climbing frame in a playground or the branch of a tree) and a mat or grass for doing exercises on. The tests are done in accordance with the instructions below, with the scores entered on a card as illustrated. All tests in Part 1 are to be completed in numerical order, with a short recovery period between each. Part 2 is done only when you are fully recovered from Part 1. To pass each fitness level (high, average or low) all test results must reach the same level; a lower grading for any one test equals a lower rating overall. High indicates that you have a high capacity for physical work that can meet most demands without stress and with good energy reserves. Average indicates that you can cope with average demands without undue fatigue and have some reserve of energy for unforeseen emergencies. Low indicates that you are able to meet daily physical demands only with difficulty and, in general, you suffer from fatigue and lack of energy. These are the six tests, all of which must be completed.

1 *Pull-ups:* the pull-up is primarily a measure of the endurance of the muscle group responsible for flexion of the forearm. The subject grasps a horizontal bar with both hands, palms forward ie overgrasp. From the 'dead hang' position the body is pulled up until the chin is above the top of the bar and is then lowered until the arms are fully extended. The process is repeated until the subject can no longer pull his chin above the bar. The knees may not be raised, nor is kicking permitted. The number of repetitions is recorded.

2 *Burpees:* the burpee (bend and thrust) is a test of muscular endurance involving many large muscle groups. Rapid movements that involve changes in body position are emphasised. The subject stands at attention with feet together and hands at the sides. The squat position is then assumed, with the hands placed on the floor adjacent to the feet. The legs are thrust to the rear as the subject assumes the front support position (body perfectly straight). The feet are then brought back to the squat position and then the body returns to the standing position. As many repetitions as possible are performed in 1 minute.

3 *Sit-ups:* the bent-leg sit-up is a measure of the muscular endurance of the abdominal muscles. These muscles are very important in maintaining good posture. The subject lies on the back with the fingers interlocked behind the neck. Both feet are placed flat on the floor and the knees are flexed, forming an angle of approximately 90° with the feet held firmly in place; the subject sits up so that the elbow touches the opposite knee alternately. Each time the subject returns to the starting position, the fingers behind the neck must come into contact with the floor, and must remain behind the neck when he sits up. The process is repeated as many times as possible in 1 minute.

4 *Dorsal raise:* the dorsal raise is a measure of the muscular endurance of the dorsal muscles. These muscles contribute greatly to good posture. The subject lies face down with the arms placed behind the back and hands clasped. The head, arms, chest and legs are raised clear of the floor as high as possible, and then returned to the ground. The knees should not bend and the legs should be kept straight. The process is repeated as many times as possible in 1 minute.

5 *Push-ups:* the push-up is a measure of the endurance of the muscle group concerned with extension of the forearm. The subject assumes a prone position on the floor with the hands directly under the shoulder joints, legs straight and together, and the arms straight. The subject then lowers the body until the chest touches the floor and then pushes with the arms until they are fully extended. The body is kept in a straight line from the head to the toes throughout the movement. There is no limit for this test, but the push-ups must be performed continuously.

6 *2·4km (1½-Mile) run:* this test measures cardiovascular endurance, one of the most important factors of physical fitness, the lack of which is the reason why a person reaches the point at which his body cannot process sufficient oxygen to supply the energy needed to perform the task.

PART 1

	Test 1	Test 2	Test 3	Test 4	Test 5
FITNESS LEVEL	PULL-UPS (Max)	BURPEES (1min)	SIT-UPS (1min)	DORSAL (1min)	PUSH-UPS (1min)
High	11-15	31-40	41-50	41-50	41-50
	....	....	....	....	....
Average	6-10	21-30	31-40	31-40	31-40
	....	....	....	....	....
Low	0-5	0-20	0-30	0-30	0-30
	....	....	....	....	....

PART 2

2·4km (1½ -Mile) Run		Time Recorded
High	9min or below	....
Average	9·01-10min	....
Low	10·01min and above	....

Fitness Level (Part 1) ....

Fitness Level (Part 2) ....

Areas of Weakness ....

All that is required to improve your physical fitness is the space to progressively exercise all the main muscle groups, the heart and lungs. You do not need a well equipped sports centre, but you do need the right mental attitude — the conviction that you want to be fitter. The methods described here will be effective if you put in the work. First, though, a word about running, which should be woven into the programme of workouts; two runs a week between three exercise days followed by two rest days would be a reasonable plan.

A lot of over-use injuries are caused by poor footwear. A good training shoe will have a shock-absorbing spongy sole, a heel elevated at least 2·5mm (½in) to take the pressure off your Achilles tendon, and a good arch to prevent the foot rolling over, which can put pressure on the knee joint. It must, of course, be long enough to give the big toe movement, and also broad enough to accommodate the width of the foot — a point sometimes overlooked. The best natural running surface is a woodland trail with a carpet of dead leaves and detritus to absorb foot impact, but trails are not as plentiful as roads and concrete pavements, which make the worst running tracks as they increase the risk of stress injury. If you are not near open countryside and footpaths then try and run in a park, a local common or along the grass verges of roads. When you must run on roads keep off the camber as much as possible.

Style is all important to economical and enjoyable running. Beginners often make the mistake of overstriding and hitting the ground with the heel first. The correct way is a glide of the body when the sole and heel of both shoes become worn equally. If the upper part of the body is tensed it will add to fatigue and cause more energy drain. The arms should swing in a relaxed motion across the body at, or just above, waist level with the hands cupped but not clenched. Carry your head upright and as still as possible with your eyes focussed about 10m (11yd) in front of you. Also keep your shoulders up and centred over the hips; they should move gently in time with your stride.

There is no need to try to run 110 to 160km (70 to 100 miles) a week; 24 to 32km (15 to 20 miles) is quite adequate to maintain cardiovascular fitness when combined with exercise workouts. Most people who are uninitiated fall down on their preparation for anything physical, and going for a run is no exception. To don PT rig when you get home from work and just go out running and using muscles that have been sitting around all day without giving them a warm-up is asking for trouble. They will start aching afterwards and stiffen up; the effect will probably be worse when you get up in the morning, which is a sure sign that the body was not prepared. Always do a few gentle stretching exercises before a run to warm the muscles and stimulate the synovial fluid, which is the 'lubricating oil' for your joints. Also do some gentle exercises when finished so that the muscles do not tighten up suddenly.

Free-standing circuit training, which requires no equipment, is the ideal way for small groups, or even the individual working on his own, to organise PT workouts in the correct physiological manner. Each session consists of three phases: the warm-up, the main activity, and cooling-down or finishing exercises. The warm-up increases circulation, warms the muscles, prepares them for harder work to follow, and prevents tearing and pulling. It will lessen the amount of stiffness that can follow exercise and at the same time gets you mentally in the mood for the work in hand. The warm-up itself is in two parts — light mobility exercises and stretching exercises. Mobility exercises start from the top of the body and work down to the legs, as shown in this table, which you should aim to run through twice during a warm-up session:

Arms & shoulders: with feet apart and fingertips touching the shoulders, circle the elbows forwards and backwards.

Trunk bending: with feet wide apart and hands on the hips, bend the trunk from side to side.

Trunk twisting: with feet wide apart and hands on the hips, twist the body around to the left and right alternately.

Forward twisting: with feet wide apart and the body bent forward, twist it to touch the left toe with the right fingertips, then the right toe with the left fingertips.

Supple exercise: with the feet wide apart and the body bent forward, touch the ground in front of, between and behind the legs then return to the upright position.

Leg exercise: standing erect graps each knee alternately to the chest.

Arms & shoulders: with feet slightly apart circle the arms forwards and backwards.

Trunk bending: with feet wide apart bend the trunk from side to side while tucking the opposite hand into the armpit.

Forward twisting: with the feet apart and the trunk bent forward turn the head and shoulders and swing the arms from side to side.

Trunk twisting: with the feet wide apart and the hands clasped behind the neck, twist the body to left and right alternately.

Supple exercise: with the feet wide apart and arms bent upwards stretch the arms above the head, then bend the trunk and touch the toes. Return to the start position in the reverse order.

Leg exercise: with the feet slightly apart and hands on the hips, bend the knees and stretch first one leg then the other. The knees should be bent to the half squat position only; full bend knee exercises should be avoided.

Regular stretching exercises reduce the possibility of pulled or strained muscles and the onset of stiffness afterwards, and increase flexibility and agility. The following should be performed in sequence:

Upper body, arms and shoulders: stand with the feet slightly apart and with the arms above the head, then clasp the hands palms out. Stretch the arms as far as possible, locking the elbows inwards.

Shoulders and triceps: with the feet slightly apart, clasp one elbow behind the neck and pull it in a downward movement. Repeat the exercise on the other elbow.

Sides of the body: with the feet wide apart and the hands clasped behind the neck, lean the body to the left for the count of 3 and then to the right.

The chest: with the feet slightly apart, body erect and hands clasped behind the back, straighten the arms and then lift them up behind the back and lock them to expand the chest.

Hamstrings: with the feet wide apart, bend down and grasp the ankles. Hold the position while bracing back on the knees and force the head between the legs as far as possible. Repeat the exercise with the feet closer together. Then repeat yet again with one foot crossed over the other.

Groin: assume a crouching position, with the hands flat on the ground and one leg extended sideways. Hold the position, keeping the extended leg straight and the knee braced back. Repeat with the other leg.

Hamstrings: sitting with the legs apart, grasp first the left then the right ankle keeping the leg straight and knee braced, then try to get the head down to the knee. Repeat the exercise with the legs together and grasping both ankles.

Thigh: adopting the 'hurdling' position lean back as far as possible while keeping the knee of the bent, or hurdle, leg to the ground. Go back as far as you can until you feel the pull on the thigh of the bent leg.

Achilles tendon: standing with one foot forward and the other back, push against a wall or solid object while keeping the rear leg straight and its heel flat on the ground.

Stretching exercises need to be done with some care. Always go slowly into a stretch and come out of it slowly. Never force it and never, never bounce in the stretch position. Only go into a stretch as far as it is comfortable and then hold it for 10 to 15 seconds. If you do bounce in an effort to increase the stretch you will aggravate the myotonic reflex (which is the safety mechanism in muscle) and it will hurt, which is its way of telling you to stop or ease off. If you persist in bouncing through the pain you will get muscle soreness and may even tear it and end up needing the physiotherapist. Make sure you always stretch each limb in all directions. If your stretching is poor to start with, it will improve and become easier the more you do the exercises.

The main activity following a warm-up may be a run, crosscountry walk, some backpacking or any other endurance training. A free standing circuit can be completed in about 20 minutes and consists of a series of 8 to 10 different exercises, which are each repeated a number of times. To start off the group (or individual) runs round a circle about 10 to 15m (11 to 16yd) diameter in a counter-clockwise direction and on the command '15 push-ups, start', or whatever exercise is chosen, the group stops running, faces inwards and does the exercise the stipulated number of times. As each individual completes his number he starts running round the circle. When everybody is running again the next exercise is called, and so on until the programme is completed. Then everybody does a series of very fast stop-start 33m (30yd) sprints. The circuit with its sprints should be completed three times in a session with time allowed between each circuit for breathing exercises. A set time limit instead of a number of repeats can be given for each exercise, say 10 to 15 seconds. Doing it that way each individual can keep a count over a period of how many repeats he averages in a set time at each session, which will indicate improving physical efficiency. A large kitchen clock with an easily visible second hand is the one piece of equipment that could well be used. Naturally it takes three or more people to form anything like a circle, but someone on his own or two persons can do a circuit calling out their own orders and using chairs, books, stones or whatever, to mark out a rough circle for running round, indoors or out. Never leave out the cooling-down or finishing-off period of light mobility and stretching-with-breathing exercises.

The eight exercises illustrated would make a good circuit series for the beginner and relatively unfit person with a sedentary life style:

1 *Arm exercise; arm swinging with heel raising:* swing the arms up vigorously to the level of the shoulders, palms turned down, reaching out sideways as far as possible. At the same time rise on the toes. Then swing the arms to the side and lower the heels.

2 *Trunk suppling exercise; knee grasping to chest:* keep the body upright and grasp each knee alternately as tightly as possible to the chest with the hands round the lower leg.

Fig 1   Circuit training, exercises 1-8

3   *Leg exercise; knee stretching from crouch position:* start with the knees fully bent, hands flat on the ground and head up. Keep the hands as nearly as possible where they are and stretch the knees vigorously and tuck the head in. Return slowly to the starting position.

4   *Arm exercise; double arm circling:* with fists clenched, swing both arms at the same time in a circle forward, upward and backward to the starting position in one continuous movement. The circle is described slowly and repeated a number of times.

5   *Trunk suppling exercise; arm stretching combined with trunk bending:* with feet wide apart and arms bent, go through these four movements—stretch the arms upwards; re-bend the arms to the starting position; keeping the knees straight, bend the trunk forward and downward and stretch the arms to touch the toes. Return to the starting position.

6   *Leg exercise; knee full bending with arm swinging forward:* from a standing position sink down on the heels allowing the knees to bend forward, and at the same time swing the arms loosely forward. The arms reach the level of the shoulders as the knees are fully bent, and return to the side as the knees are stretched.

7   *Arm exercise; arm stretching upward and sideways:* stand with arms bent, then stretch them vigorously upward. Bend them to the starting position. Stretch them vigorously sideways, then bend them to the starting position.

8   *Trunk suppling exercise; arm swinging forward with hand kicking:* stand with the arms raised sideways in line with the shoulders and palms turned down. Swing both arms forwards, at the same time kicking the palms with one foot. Part the arms and then repeat with the other leg. Both legs should be kept straight and the body upright.

Do five 33m (30yd) sprints.

For serious training, the circuit should be done daily with each exercise repeated 30 times, followed by the sprints. The repetitions can be increased by up to an extra 10 each week with a maximum of 60 repetitions, and the number of sprints increased by 1 a week up to a total of 200m (220yd).

An alternative method of physical training, known as 5BX, is used throughout the Royal Marines Corps for where space is limited — for example on board the Commando carriers. Originally devised by the Royal Canadian Air Force, this method was adopted by the Royal Navy, of which the Royal Marines are a part. It provides a programme of PT for anyone who has neither the time for any of the conventional forms of physical activity nor the gymnastic facilities to work at the more scientific systems of fitness training. The 5BX exercises require an allotted time of 11 minutes a day. There are six separate charts to work from, and each of them sets twelve progressive levels of work. No apparatus is needed; everything can be done in a small space and in complete privacy (except for the runs and walks for which you have to go outside; in the Navy personnel run round the ship). The exercises are suitable for anyone up to 60 years of age, and the charts allow the unfit person to start at the level of his ability and then progress up to one adequate for his age. Before starting on this system, remember that the repetitions of the five exercises on each chart must be completed in the allotted time, and performed correctly, of course. Progress should be at the rate set out below. *(Note:* the grade A + in Chart 6 is at international athlete level).

How to Progress
20 years, at least 1 day at each level
20 to 29 years, at least 2 days at each level
30 to 39 years, at least 4 days at each level
40 to 49 years, at least 7 days at each level
50 to 59 years, at least 8 days at each level
60 years and over, at least 10 days at each level

If you feel stiff or sore, or if you are unduly breathless at any time, ease up or slow down your rate of progression. This is particularly applicable to the older age groups. Even if you feel able to start at a high level and progress at a faster rate than indicated — *don't do it.* Start at the bottom of Chart 1 and work up from level to level as recommended.

Chart 1

Fig 2   5BX exercises, Chart 1

Chart 1

Exercise 1: feet astride, arms upwards. Forward bend to touch floor, upward stretch and bend trunk backwards. *Note:* keep the knees straight when touching the floor. If you are unable to touch the floor, try to press down as far as possible each time.

Exercise 2: lie flat, feet 15cm (6in) apart, arms to the side. Sit up to just see your feet, then return to lying position.

Exercise 3: lie on stomach with palms placed under the thighs. Raise head and one leg, repeat raising alternate leg. *Note:* keep the leg straight at the knee, thighs must clear the palms of the hands. Count one each time the second leg touches the floor.

Exercise 4: lie on stomach, hands under the shoulders with palms flat on the floor. Straighten arms lifting upper body, keeping the knees on the floor. Bend arms to lower the body. *Note:* keep the body straight from the knees, arms must be fully extended, and chest must touch the floor to complete one movement.

Exercise 5: stationary run (count a step each time the left foot touches the ground, lift feet approximately 10cm (4in) off the floor). Every 75 steps do 10 scissor jumps. Repeat the sequence until the required number of steps is completed. Scissor jumps—stand with right leg and left arm extended forwards, and left leg and right arm extended backwards. Jump up and change position of arms and legs before landing, repeat (arms shoulder high).

Physical Capacity Rating Scale for Chart 1							
Level	EXERCISE					·8km (½mile) run	1·6km (1 mile) walk
	1	2	3	4	5	mins	mins
A+	20	18	22	13	400	5½	17
A	18	17	20	12	375	5½	17
A−	16	15	18	11	355	5½	17
B+	14	13	16	9	320	6	18
B	12	12	14	8	305	6	18
B−	10	11	12	7	280	6	18
C+	8	9	10	6	260	6½	19
C	7	8	9	5	235	6½	19
C−	6	7	8	4	205	6½	19
D+	4	5	6	3	175	7	20
D	3	4	5	3	145	7½	21
D−	2	3	4	2	100	8	21
	2	1	1	1	6	(minutes for each exercise)	

Chart 2

Fig 3   5BX exercises, Chart 2

Chart 2

Exercise 1: feet apart, arms upwards. Touch the floor, press down, stretch upwards, then bend trunk backwards. *Note:* keep the legs straight.

Exercise 2: lie flat on the floor, feet 15cm (6in) apart and arms at the sides. Sit up to vertical position keeping feet on the floor. Return to lying position. *Note:* feet may be secured by fixing under a chair.

Exercise 3: lie on stomach with palms under the thighs. Raise head, shoulders and both legs. Return to lying position. *Note:* keep the legs straight, and both thighs must clear the hands.

Exercise 4: lie on stomach with hands under the shoulders, palms flat on the floor. Straighten the arms to lift the body with only palms and toes on the floor and keeping the back straight. *Note:* the chest must touch the floor after the arms have been fully extended to complete the movement.

Exercise 5: stationary run (count a step each time the left foot touches the floor—lift feet approximately 10cm (4in) off the floor). After 75 steps do 10 astride jumps. Repeat this sequence until the required number of steps is completed. Astride jumps—feet together, arms at sides. Jump up with legs apart and the arms swinging upwards and sideways to above shoulder height, then return to starting position. *Note:* keep the arms straight.

Physical Capacity Rating Scale for Chart 2						1·6 (1 mile) run	3·2km (2 mile) walk
Level	EXERCISE					mins	mins
	1	2	3	4	5		
A+	30	23	33	20	500	9	30
A	29	21	31	19	485	9	31
A−	28	20	29	18	470	9	32
B+	26	18	27	17	455	9½	33
B	24	17	25	16	455	9½	33
B−	22	16	23	15	440	9½	33
C+	20	15	21	14	425	10	34
C	19	14	19	13	410	10	34
C−	18	13	17	12	395	10	34
D+	16	12	15	11	380	10½	35
D	15	11	14	10	360	10½	35
D−	14	10	13	9	335	10½	35
	2	1	1	1	6	(minutes for each exercise)	

Chart 3

Exercise 1

Exercise 2

Exercise 3

Exercise 4

Exercise 5

Fig 4   5BX exercises, Chart 3

32

Chart 3

Exercise 1: feet apart arms upwards. Touch the floor 15cm (6in) outside left foot, again between feet, press down once then 15cm (6in) outside right foot, bend backwards as far as possible, then repeat in the reverse order after half the number of counts. *Note:* keep the legs straight at all times.

Exercise 2: lie flat, feet 15cm (6in) apart and hands clasped behind the head. Sit up to vertical position keeping feet on the floor. *Note:* feet may be secured under a chair, but only if really necessary.

Exercise 3: lie on the stomach with hands interlocked behind the back. Lift head, shoulders, chest and both legs as high as possible. *Note:* keep legs straight, and raise chest and both thighs completely off the floor.

Exercise 4: lie on the stomach with the hands under the shoulders and palms flat on the floor. Touch the floor with the chin in front of the hands, straighten arms and legs and raise back, then touch floor with the forehead behind the hands, straighten body. *Note:* there are three definite movements—chin, forehead, arms straight. Do *not* do in one continuous movement.

Exercise 5: stationary run (count a step each time the left foot touches the floor—lift the feet approximately 10cm (4in) off the floor). After every 75 steps do 10 bobbing jumps. Repeat this sequence until the required number of steps is completed. Bobbing jumps—feet together hands on hips, knees bent to sit on heels. Straighten to upright position raising heels off the floor, return to starting position each time. Keep the feet in contact with the floor, the back upright and straight at all times.

Physical Capacity Rating Scale for Chart 3							
Level	EXERCISE					·8km (½mile) run	1·6km (1 mile) walk
	1	2	3	4	5	mins	mins
A+	30	32	47	24	550	8	25
A	30	31	45	22	540	8	25
A−	30	30	43	21	525	8	25
B+	28	28	41	20	510	8½	26
B	28	27	39	19	500	8½	26
B−	28	26	37	18	490	8½	26
C+	26	25	35	17	480	8½	27
C	26	24	34	17	465	8½	27
C−	26	23	33	16	450	8½	27
D+	24	22	31	15	430	8½	28
D	24	21	30	15	415	8½	28
D−	24	20	29	15	400	8½	29
	2	1	1	1	6	(minutes for each exercise)	

Chart 4

Fig 5   5BX exercises, Chart 4

Chart 4

Exercise 1: feet apart, arms upwards. Touch the floor with both hands outside the left foot, between the feet and press down once, then outside the right foot. Straighten up and circle the trunk backwards as far as possible with the arms up above the head. Reverse the direction after half the number of counts. *Note:* keep the legs straight, and bend backwards past the vertical each time.

Exercise 2: lie on back with legs straight, feet together and arms straight above the head. Sit up and touch the toes keeping arms and legs straight. Feet may be fixed, but only if really necessary. *Note:* keep arms in contact with the side of the head throughout the exercise.

Exercise 3: lie on stomach with arms stretched sideways. Lift head, shoulders, arms, chest and both legs as high as possible. *Note:* keep legs straight, raise chest and both thighs completely off the floor.

Exercise 4: lie on stomach with the palms of the hands flat on the floor approximately 30cm (12in) from the ears. Straighten the arms to lift the body. *Note:* the chest must touch the floor after each movement.

Exercise 5: stationary run (count a step each time the left foot touches the floor—lift knees waist high). Every 75 steps do 10 squat jumps. Repeat this sequence until the required number of steps is completed. Squat jumps — right foot slightly forward, knees bent, fingertips touching the floor outside the feet. Jump to upright position while reversing the position of the feet. Return to starting position with the left foot forward. *Note:* touch the floor with the fingertips, feet must completely clear the floor. Keep back straight at all times.

Physical Capacity Rating Scale for Chart 4						
Level	EXERCISE					1·6km (1 mile) run	3·2km (2 mile) walk
	1	2	3	4	5	mins	mins
A+	30	22	50	42	400	7	19
A	30	22	49	40	395	7	19
A−	30	22	49	37	390	7	19
B+	28	21	47	34	380	7½	20
B	28	21	46	32	375	7½	20
B−	28	21	46	30	365	7½	20
C+	26	19	44	28	355	7½	21
C	26	19	43	26	345	7½	21
C−	26	19	43	24	335	7½	21
D+	24	18	41	19	315	7½	23
D	24	18	40	19	315	7½	23
D−	24	18	40	17	300	7½	23
	2	1	1	1	6	(minutes for each exercise)	

Chart 5

Exercise 1

Exercise 2

Exercise 3

Exercise 4

Exercise 5

Fig 6   5BX exercises, Chart 5

Chart 5

Exercise 1: feet apart, arms upwards and straight, hands clasped. Touch the floor with both hands outside the left foot, between the feet and press down once, then outside the right foot. Straighten up and circle the trunk backwards as far as possible. Reverse the direction after half the number of counts. *Note:* keep the legs and arms straight at all times.

Exercise 2: lie on back with the legs straight, feet together and hands clasped under the head. Sit up and bend the knees; at the same time twist the trunk to touch the left knee with the right elbow. This completes one movement. Alternate the direction of twist each time. *Note:* keep the feet off the floor when touching elbow to knee.

Exercise 3: lie on stomach with arms extended over the head. Raise the arms, head, chest and both legs as high as possible. *Note:* keep the legs and arms straight, and lift the chest and both thighs completely off the floor.

Exercise 4: lie on stomach, hands under the shoulders with the palms flat on the floor. Push up off the floor and clap hands before returning to the starting position. *Note:* keep the body straight during the entire movement. Hand clap must be heard.

Exercise 5: stationary run (count a step each time the left foot touches the floor, lift knees waist high). Every 75 steps do 10 spread eagle jumps. Repeat this sequence until the required number of steps is completed. Spread eagle jumps — feet together, knees bent, sit on the heels, fingertips touching the floor. Jump in the air with legs apart and swing the arms overhead in mid-air. Return directly to the starting position on landing. *Note:* raise the hands above head level, spread feet at least shoulder-width apart before landing.

Physical Capacity Rating Scale for Chart 5						
Level	EXERCISE					1·6km (1 mile) run
	1	2	3	4	5	mins · secs
A+	30	40	50	44	500	6 · 00
A	30	39	49	43	485	6 · 06
A−	30	38	48	42	475	6 · 09
B+	28	36	47	40	465	6 · 12
B	28	35	46	39	455	6 · 15
B−	28	34	45	38	445	6 · 21
C+	26	32	44	36	435	6 · 27
C	26	31	43	35	420	6 · 33
C−	26	28	42	34	410	6 · 39
D+	24	28	41	32	400	6 · 45
D	24	27	40	31	385	6 · 51
D−	24	26	39	30	375	7 · 00
	2	1	1	1	6	(minutes for each exercise)

Chart 6

Fig 7   5BX exercises, Chart 6

Chart 6

Exercise 1: feet apart, arms upwards and straight, hands reverse clasped. Touch the floor with both hands outside the left foot, then between the feet and press down once, then outside the right foot. Circle the trunk backwards as far as possible. Reverse the direction after half the number of counts. *Note:* keep the legs and arms straight, and hands tightly clasped at all times.

Exercise 2: lie flat with legs straight, feet together and arms straight over the head. Sit up and, at the same time, lift both legs and touch the toes so that the body forms a V-shape. *Note:* keep the feet together and legs and arms straight; all of the upper back and legs clear the floor and the fingers touch the toes each time.

Exercise 3: lie on stomach with arms extended over the head. Raise the arms, head, chest and both legs as high as possible, then press back once. *Note:* keep the legs and arms straight; chest and both thighs are raised completely off the floor.

Exercise 4: lie on stomach with hands under the shoulders, the palms flat on the floor. Push up off the floor and slap the chest before returning to the starting position. *Note:* keep the body straight during the entire movement; the chest slap must be heard.

Exercise 5: stationary run (count a step every time the left foot touches the floor, lift knees waist high). Every 75 steps do 10 jack jumps. Repeat this until the required number of steps is completed. Jack jumps—feet together, knees bent, sit on heels, fingertips touching the floor. Jump up, raise the legs waist high and touch the toes in mid-air.

	Physical Capacity Rating Scale for Chart 6					
Level	EXERCISE					1·6km (1 mile) run
	1	2	3	4	5	mins · secs
A+	30	50	40	40	600	5 · 00
A	30	48	39	39	580	5 · 03
A−	30	47	38	38	555	5 · 09
B+	28	45	37	36	530	5 · 12
B	28	44	36	35	525	5 · 18
B−	28	43	35	34	515	5 · 24
C+	26	41	34	32	505	5 · 27
C	26	40	33	31	495	5 · 33
C−	26	39	32	30	485	5 · 39
D+	24	37	31	28	475	5 · 45
D	24	36	30	27	460	5 · 51
D−	24	35	29	26	450	6 · 00
	2	1	1	1	6	(minutes for each exercise)

There are some risks in undertaking hard physical exercise in extremely hot weather if you are not acclimatised. Under normal conditions heat loss from the body is 67 per cent by radiation, 10 per cent by conduction-convection and 23 per cent by evaporation (sweat). The increase in body temperature through exercise is directly related to the intensity of the effort demanded of the individual. If heat from exercise is added to environmental heat, the body has to compensate through conduction-convection and evaporation to cool it down. If the body has difficulty in dissipating the increasing heat, dangerous problems can arise. As the body temperature rises, certain physical symptoms develop. At a body (rectal) temperature of 40 to 40·6°C (104 to 105°F) there will be a throbbing pressure in the temples and a cold sensation over the trunk. With a temperature rise of another degree to 41·1°C (106°F) there will be muscular weakness, disorientation and loss of equilibrium. Above 41·1°C (106°F) sweating will decrease and there will be loss of consciousness; this stage can be fatal. Anyone who experiences those first symptoms, while exercising in heat, is approaching a harmful state and should stop immediately and lower the body temperature by getting into cool water, or at least drinking a lot of cool fluid. Collapse from overheating is a dangerous condition and a victim must be immediately submerged in cool water to which ice can be added to avoid straining the heart. The danger is greater for large people who lead sedentary lives and carry a lot of body fat.

Our bodies contain about 60 per cent water, which plays a major part in maintaining constant body temperature. Sweating, which helps to keep us cool, càn reach a level of about a litre (nearly one quart) per hour. Water lost through sweating must be replaced or there will be a drop in the essential water content of the muscles and a collapse of the blood circulatory system because there will be insufficient blood to reach all parts of the body. Water is always a better fluid replacement than bottled or canned drinks which contain too much sugar to enable water replacement to be fully effective. A small amount of salt on food and the eating of green vegetables are both important in this context to maintain the ratio of sodium and potassium in the system. To keep the body temperature down, while exercising in the heat, it is essential to increase the sweat rate, but this can only be achieved by acclimatisation so that the body will start to sweat at a lower temperature. The way to become acclimatised is to exercise at half one's normal effort for about an hour in the heat of the day for twelve consecutive days — all the time keeping alert for any signs of heat exhaustion. Training in cooler times of the day will not effect a perfect acclimatisation, and if work in the heat is stopped for two weeks or more it will be necessary to re-acclimatise. At all times water replacement is critical, with a 2 per cent loss of weight from sweating being the maximum that can be tolerated. A 4 per cent loss can lead to serious sickness. A fit person will sweat more frequently than one who is unfit and who is more at risk in heat and will take longer to acclimatise.

Although the Marines use no set table of exercises for a climber, he does need to keep himself fit and upper body strength is most important. Mountain Leaders in the Commando forces appreciate that technique alone cannot always prevail, and that obstacles such as overhangs can soon sap strength. So they include plenty of pull-ups and press-ups in their fitness programme. Fingers need to be strong, and finger strength can also be achieved by fingertip press-ups and pull-ups. Sports shops sell finger exercisers which are basically springs which one squeezes and releases; a firm rubber ball is an acceptable substitute.

To develop the right muscles for climbing the best training is to get onto a rock which need only be a boulder or small crag a few feet off the ground, or an indoor climbing wall at a sports centre. Multi-gyms with their weight training apparatus offer all the facilities to improve upper body strength. Or you could emulate the 'torture' imposed on Commandos undergoing their Mountain Leader courses when they have to run with arms outstretched holding a good sized stone (weighing a few pounds) in each hand. The same exercise can be done while stationary; either way it is a good method of building up arm and shoulder muscles. Whilst improving strength, it is important to remain supple and agile so plenty of stretching and loosening-up exercises should be included in a session.

CHAPTER 3

WALKING TO FITNESS

As walking accounts for nine-tenths of all outdoor activity it is an important part of any training programme and is, of course, an excellent form of exercise in its own right. Fortunately it is something that can be done virtually anywhere and at any time. A good way of training is to walk to and from work or, if that is too far to be practical, to use a bicycle. Cycling strengthens the leg muscles, as well as the upper limbs and the lungs when done under pressure. Aim to increase speed over a period of time, especially going uphill. A paper round, for those who are young enough, is a profitable form of training, and the early morning starts are good for self-discipline. Like everything else, walking should be done on a regular basis and progressively increased as the leg muscles get more used to it. After two or three weeks, put a small backpack on with a few things in it and then increase the loading over a period. Training walks should be done in the shoes or boots you will wear in the field.

From walking you can go on to what in the services is called speed marching—used to get a body of men fast from A to B at a pace that leaves them fit to fight, not to drop. Set a target of, say, 5km (3 miles) in 30 minutes and pace yourself running and walking to do it in exactly that time, not 27 minutes and not 35. In open country this means running on the flat and walking uphill. There is a pain barrier, a stitch, which is nothing to do with ligaments or joints and you will soon recognise it as something you can pass through. Stretching exercises before walking and running will help to get rid of chest pain—which is the intercostal muscles between the ribs objecting to unaccustomed work—and make breathing a lot easier. For the townsman a very accessible, strenuous but boring form of hill walking is the staircase of a block of flats. Running up and walking down is a recognised form of interval training and provides a good opportunity of judging your fitness through your pulse rate. Take your resting pulse first, then work it up to a high rate, and time how long it takes to go back down to normal. The shorter the time the better, and as that time shortens during training so, it is hoped, will you be getting fitter. This pulse test can be done with lots of other forms of exercise as well.

If you want to find out how your fitness compares with the least active of the Marines (clerks, cooks, drivers and the like) give yourself their Battle Fitness Test, which men in those jobs have to pass every six months. If they fail, they have to go for compulsory physical training in their own time until they do pass. The test is the rock bottom acceptable level of fitness, and any self-respecting Marine would expect to pass with ease. It consists of a 2·5km (1½-mile) forced march, alternating quick marching and running, which is done as a squad or group. That is followed by a 2·5km (1½-mile) individual best effort run which must, according to age, be completed within the following times:

29 and under	11½ min
30 to 34	12 min
35 to 39	13 min
40 and over	14 min

Both runs are done in boots but without equipment; it would be cheating to wear training or running shoes.

CHAPTER 4

CLOTHES FOR THE JOB

Today there is no excuse, other than lack of money, for being improperly dressed or ill-equipped for any outdoor activity be it a walk along a coastal path or a climbing expedition to the high Andes. Ski-, climbing- and sports-gear shops have proliferated in the last two decades, as have the quality and variety of products available. There have been enormous improvements in material technology and protective clothing; camping and sleeping kit are not only more efficient, but weigh a fraction of what they did only a few years ago. The best advice on clothing and equipment is to be had from longtime users. Ask someone with experience, and in whom you have confidence, what they recommend and why. Price and personal preference are bound to be part of that advice, so try and get a cross-section of opinions. Many shops are owned and run by people with a lifetime's experience and a successful track record in one or more outdoor sports.

Of all the clothing you buy, be most particular about your boots. You will not enjoy anything if your feet hurt, and badly fitting footwear cannot only damage your feet but have a knock-on effect, upsetting your whole balance and rhythm. When shopping for boots take along the socks you will normally wear with them. Get the right boots for the job and the best that your money will buy. Looked after, they will last for very many years and become comfortable old friends. There are dozens of brand names and several qualities to choose from, but they can all be divided into three main types:

1 *Mountain climbing boots* have one-piece leather uppers with bellow or overlap tongues, narrow welts, pointed toes, hook fastenings or rings for laces, and rigid Vibram cleated rubber soles. There are numerous styles, but the main point is to have

a rigid sole that will support you and give security and confidence on small footholds. They are difficult and tiring for long walking. A good insole is most important to give added insulation and comfort. Polystyrene is a popular material for this purpose.

2 *Walking boots* have much the same features as mountain climbing boots except that they have flexible soles. Most types do not have quite such good insulation, nor are they as waterproof as climbing boots. If a lot of walking is to be done, the waterproof quality of a boot is most important and should not be compromised for price. Walking dry shod is not a luxury, it is being wise. Depending on how stiff the soles are, good walking boots can be used for elementary rock climbing and scrambling. Training shoes are not walking boots. The young and light of foot with a good sense of balance often cover the roughest ground in training shoes, but they do it unprotected and are at risk of straining or breaking an ankle.

3 *Rock climbing boots* look a bit like old-fashioned gym shoes that went out with long johns and twirled moustaches. They are lightweight, designed exclusively for climbing rocks, and are tight fitting to enable the climber to 'feel' the rock surface. The uppers are canvas or suede, and the very tough smooth rubber soles overlap the foot and give an excellent grip on smooth rock. These boots are also known as friction boots.

All boots will last much longer if you clean them and remove stones from the soles; give the uppers a light coating of silicone wax or polish (where appropriate) to keep them supple and waterproof but not too much or too often or the leather will become too soft and pliable to give support. Before going out, inspect them for broken soles, worn-out treads, dry and cracked leather, rotten stitching and broken fastening hooks. Also, of course, check for frayed laces — how embarrassing, or worse, if they break halfway between heaven and earth. (*Memo:* always keep a spare pair in your backpack). Wet boots should be stuffed with newspaper and left to dry in a warm airy place away from direct heat, which will bake and crack the leather. It is a good precaution in winter to rub silicone or wax over bootlaces to prevent them freezing when they become wet. All this talk of leather—some of the best of the good walking boots are now made with fabric uppers. They can never take a polish, look awful when they get wet, and some people say they smell, but they are light and bliss to wear.

To get the most out of good boots you also need good socks; all-wool loop pile are the best although a mixture of up to 25 per cent man-made fibre is acceptable. Woollen sweaters, thick and thin, are the basis of an outdoor wardrobe, but you should avoid getting them wet in very cold conditions because the heat lost from the body in attempting to dry the wool can become a contributory factor in hypothermia. Although woollen trousers or breeches are warm and better than jeans (although many people wear the latter) they are not practical in snow and ice conditions as snow will stick to, and eventually soak into, the wool. Terylene/cotton gaberdine type weaves are best because they are windproof, have a low moisture absorption rate and they dry quickly. Of course they require something warm underneath. Wool traps insulating air in its fibres, but to keep you warm that trapped air must not be allowed to escape or be chilled by the wind, which is why outer garments need to be of a windproof fabric and preferably waterproof too. Until recently windproof and waterproof materials tended to build up condensation. New technology has produced materials like Gore-Tex which allow moisture to escape to the outside and evaporate but will not allow any in. They are waterproof but able to breathe. These fabrics are relatively expensive, but make life much more comfortable and are a definite contribution to survival in wet and cold weather.

The Arctic winters are much harsher than anything experienced in Britain, but a lot of the time the temperature fluctuates between – 10°C (14°F) and zero (32°F) and sometimes it thaws and rains. Similar climatic conditions obtain for shorter periods during any winter on the Brecon Beacons, in Snowdonia, the Pennines, the Highlands of Scotland and on such exposed open ground as Dartmoor, Exmoor, the Yorkshire Moors, the Peak District and any upland or rolling moorland. So many of the lessons learnt over the years by the Commando forces in the Arctic could be usefully applied to cold weather conditions in Britain and many other regions below the Arctic Circle.

Apart from some specific protective gear used by specialist cadres, the clothes worn by Commandos in the Arctic differ very little from what can be bought in civilian shops, except that theirs are less colourful and more soldier-proof. Providing there is no strong wind or snow falling, – 10°C (14°F) is considered to be a good healthy working temperature. Arctic training stops when the temperature falls below 35°C or the windchill equivalent. Worst are the short periods of thaw and rain when everybody and everything is soaked and there is nowhere dry to go, then the inevitable happens — it freezes again. To cope with such dramatic and fickle changes of weather the Commando must rely on what he can put on his back, and there is a limit to both the bulk and the weight that he can carry. His survival, therefore, depends on his using a limited supply of clothing correctly and following sensible rules. Cold weather clothing must insulate from the environmental cold, wind and rain, and at the same time provide ventilation to prevent overheating. Any material that resists the flow of heat is an insulator, and the best insulation of all is dry air. Wool and fur are good insulators because they hold quantities of motionless or dead air in between their fibres. Several layers of medium weight clothing are warmer than one heavy garment. Using the layer method, clothing can be rapidly adjusted by merely adding or removing a layer at a time to maintain body heat balance. The outer garment must be windproof and water repellent to prevent the outside cold or damp air from displacing the trapped body-warmed still air. However, the arrangement of clothing must be designed not only to reduce body heat loss, but also to provide adjustable ventilation, because any activity will require energy, which produces heat and perspiration that fills the air spaces of the inner garments with moisture and reduces their insulating quality. Moreover, when perspiration evaporates it chills the body.

It is essential to keep clothing as dry as possible. Snow or frost should be brushed or shaken off before entering any shelter. It is impossible to entirely avoid perspiring in even the coldest weather so advantage must be taken of each and every opportunity to dry out clothing. It can be hung on a rucksack to air while under way or underneath a backpack close to the body. In extremely low temperatures, the only way to prevent boots freezing during the night is to take them into bed with you! Feet are more vulnerable to cold than other parts of the body because they perspire more readily and boots are in direct contact with cold ground or snow and are frequently wet. The rule of wearing clothing loose, and in layers, also applies to footwear, the layers being the boots and their insoles themselves and pairs of socks; boots should be of a size large enough to allow for two, if not three, pairs. Socks that are too tight will restrict circulation, as well as the layer of warm air between them, and lead to frozen feet in quite modest cold. For the same reason avoid lacing boots too tightly. At the first sign of cold feet exercise them by stamping and double-timing a few steps back and forth and flex the toes inside the boots, all to produce muscular action which will produce heat. A plentiful supply of dry socks is a must, whatever other dry clothing is carried, and whenever feet get wet socks should be changed as soon as possible and boots should also be dried as best they can. Whenever socks are changed the feet should be massaged and, if possible, washed to keep them in good condition. If washing is not practical they can be 'dry cleaned' by vigorous rubbing with a foot powder. The head and hands are also vulnerable to the cold. Woollen hats or balaclavas, which cover the ears, are the best head protection, and woollen mitts are always preferable to gloves, while leather gloves are not recommended. The toughest and hardiest Commando will not venture out on exercise in Norway without his thermal underwear. The best type of long johns and vests are made of synthetic materials, such as polypropylene or Thermalactyl because they do not absorb moisture and are lightweight.

The same rules on clothing and ventilation can be applied in summer weather to avoid overheating and heat exhaustion. Even the finest weather can change unexpectedly, and the windward side of a high hill will be a lot colder than in the valley. Carrying some spare clothing on the warmest day is no inconvenience; it goes in the day sack in which, of course, you also have your day's rations and a little extra for emergency; add some Elastoplast, if not a small first aid kit, and, if you want to score full marks, an aluminised plastic survival blanket weighing all of 85g (3oz).

CHAPTER 5

LOAD CARRYING

Adventure Technology is what one manufacturer calls his rucksack system, and this term can equally well describe all backpacks produced by leading manufacturers such as Berghaus, Karrimor and Lowe, all of which are good quality. From very simple lightweight day sacks to multi-function large capacity Alpine rucksacks, manufacturers offer quite bewildering size and design computations. There are sacks for the occasional walker and the dedicated backpacker, for the camper, the mountain climber and the cyclist. The bigger packs take a variety of zip-on or buckle-on extra pockets and attachments. For the outdoor enthusiast, who likes a good hotel bed at night, there are backpacks which can be made to look like smart hand luggage (or is it vice versa?). Capacities go from space for little more than a camera and a bar of chocolate through 25l (under 1 cu ft) to a giant 100l (3 ½ cu ft). A lot of first-timers make the mistake of buying a pack that is far too big for their needs, then proceed to fill it and so end up carrying a lot of unnecessary weight. It may be very tempting to buy a 90l (3 cu ft) pack, which will make you look like a long distance Action Man, but for most purposes a 50l (1 ¾ cu ft) capacity will suffice for expeditions up to a week or more carrying all the spare clothing and food needed.

The A-frame is a thing of the past, but the H-frame is still popular with many long distance walkers and campers. For most occasions though, the frame is just extra bulk and weight and a nuisance in the tent. For going off into the hills for a couple of days, look for something much lighter that is comfortable and has convenient pockets for small items such as gloves, chocolate or a camera that can be reached without breaking open the whole pack. Although the H-frame does a good job in distributing the weight, it has been largely overtaken by computer-designed packs with anatomically-shaped shoulder straps, hip belts and lumbar pad with internal aluminium frames; these can to some extent be shaped to suit the individual owner. If you are going to carry fairly heavy loads for long periods, then choose either an H-frame or the best of the internal framed and contoured backpacks. In addition to design and capacity there are, with many of the larger packs, different back lengths, so that they can be fitted to the individual's back as shoes are to his feet. This, together with the adjustability of the shoulder and waist straps, is all important if reasonably heavy loads are to be carried for any length of time in comfort and without causing unnecessary fatigue and back ache, even back injury.

Colour is a matter of taste; backpacks come in quite dazzling colour combinations, or there are some 'military' versions in drab olive or disruptive pattern for those who object to the blobs of fluorescent colour that nowadays decorate our hills and mountains. Anything which blends in with the natural scene is to be encouraged, but those who dress in olive green or camouflage should always have with them something very bright and colourful with which to identify their position should they ever be in trouble. A party of people in everyday greys and browns spread out on a mountainside could be quite invisible to a helicopter crew a half-kilometre (or a quarter-mile) distant.

The first rule of packing a backpack is to get everything inside, including sleeping bag. The only item that can be sensibly strapped outside, where it will get wet, is a plastic sleeping mat. Even the very best packs are not totally waterproof, although they come very near to it. Prolonged heavy rain, sleet and snow will somehow always find a way in through some fastening, so the inside needs to be waterproofed. This can be done by lining it with a large plastic bag, which can be well sealed at the top. But by far the best method is to pack different items in individual plastic bags, which can be labelled if they are not transparent. Then, when you get into your tent, you can find and extract what you want without having to scatter the entire contents onto the floor where they will probably get wet and dirty. Plastic bags are also convenient for storing soiled items. For load packing and carrying, follow these guide lines:

1 Keep your load as light as possible while carrying everything that is required for safety. The maximum load per person should be a quarter of their weight with a top figure of 22·5kg (50lb).

2 Keep the load as high as possible and adjust all straps to keep the pack close to the back. But be careful not to restrict circulation to the arms and make sure that the shoulder straps do not accidentally trap a nerve, which will produce a tingling or numbness in the fingers.

3 Items must be arranged inside to give a balanced loading, with corners of tins, footwear and other hard objects kept away from the back. Separate all items into plastic bags, with the least needed things at the bottom and the most needed at the top.

4 Put stove and fuel in side pockets, and also anything likely to be needed on the march so that it can be got at without taking the pack off. During short stops it is often more convenient and restful to keep the pack on and lie down, using it as a back rest, or sit up with it supported on a rock or log.

5 During training for an extended expedition, loads should be a little heavier than they will be for the event.

CHAPTER 6

FREEDOM WITH A TENT

With a tent on your back you will feel that you have been given the freedom of the world. Gone will be the restrictions of day walks with the inevitable return to base or turning aside to find lodgings. Instead, you will have that nice feeling of knowing you can stop when and where you want. You will experience those sunsets and dawns that cannot be seen from an hotel bedroom; and it is so much cheaper. Above all, you go can deep into country that you would never reach while dependent on hotel or hostel. But nothing is ever as simple or as perfect as writing can make it seem. Camping needs as much commonsense as any other outdoor activity if it is to be a success.

Unless you intend to be a fair-weather only camper (and who can predict fair weather, even in summer?), buy a tent that is at least graded for three seasons (spring, summer and autumn), but for good measure and for all-year-round suitability go for a four seasons' one; the day may come when you will graduate to camping in the snow. Weight is a major consideration; how much can you comfortably carry and for how long? There are one-man tents in Gore-Tex weighing as little as 1·7kg (3lb 12oz), bivi bags as light as ·54kg (19oz), and Gore-Tex bivi tents with a 1m (3ft 3in) high domed end for sitting up in which still weigh only 1·7kg (3lb 12oz) — but they are expensive. Heavier and bulkier equipment comes cheaper. Most Marine Commandos buy on the civilian market their own bivi bags as well as other equipment which prove excellent in the field, being more comfortable or lighter than the equivalent military issue. But civilian gear has the one disadvantage — it is not soldier-proof and would not suffer being routinely thrown in and out of a 4-ton truck. Several manufacturers of camping gear, especially backpacks, now either produce to MOD specifications for the services or sell their own military type versions of their civilian products. The more expensive military versions of equipment are really only warranted if needed for very rough usage.

The basic bivi bag is, in effect, a waterproof overall for a sleeping bag. Some versions have hoops, which convert it into a low profile one-man tunnel-type tent. It is ideal for the individualist, although brewing-up becomes a bit more difficult as it has to be done outside. If it rains when you are in a bivi bag, the temptation is to forget about cooking breakfast before a day's hard walking. More self-discipline is needed when you are on your own. The Gore-Tex bivi bag is one of the best items of survival equipment to carry. It is fully waterproof, windproof and very lightweight. Because it breathes, there is no condensation inside, so the sleeping bag remains dry. With a bivi bag in your rucksack you need have little fear of being benighted in the worst weather.

There is an almost bewildering choice of sleeping systems on sale, especially among sleeping bags. The cheap-and-cheerful looking bags, filled with synthetic pile or wadding, are fine for caravanning or for the holiday camp site, but are pretty useless out in the field. The first consideration, of course, is weight. Down, which will compress into a small space but fluff out again however often it is rolled up, is, for weight and bulk, the finest insulating material as long as it remains dry. When wet, it becomes a soggy lump that takes days to dry. It is the best choice for fine weather and good Alpine conditions with no threat of a thaw. Otherwise it needs to have a waterproof outer cover, which increases its bulk. The Commando forces' Arctic issue is a downfilled bag with waterproof cover which has to be left unzipped against condensation, but which keeps dry when rolled up and so can be carried on top of a rucksack. If always using a Gore-Tex bivi bag, then down is the answer, but a relatively expensive one. If you know that you will be sleeping in wet conditions (and snow holes can be very wet) then Hollofil, a man-made fibre, is the best. When it gets wet it does not absorb water but maintains pockets of air that retain warmth. When using a two-man tent the load should be divided equally if your walking stamina is about the same, but if one is a bit stronger at walking he can carry a little extra weight to balance both walking paces at the same level.

Sleeping systems are now available that use a principle similar to that of layers of clothing to provide comfortable nights in all climates. It is no longer necessary to carry one heavy bag winter and summer, or to have a heavy and lightweight one and not be certain which to use. An all-weather sleeping bag is augmented by choice of down or pile-filled inner or a brush-finished liner for cold weather, a foam mat or a self-inflating thermal mat and, over all, a Gore-Tex bivi bag to keep the all-weather sleeping bag dry, which can be used on its own with the liner in warm weather. By selective shopping the whole system can be kept to under 3·86kg (8lb 8oz). It is now possible to rough it in comfort which, put another way, means you can better endure and survive harsh conditions. This is all to the good as there never was any advantage in discomfort for its own sake.

Whenever possible, plan from the map where you will camp, taking into account what you are going to do the next day. Choose a place that will have a nice atmosphere, is near a water supply and sheltered from the wind. Avoid having to look for a site at the last minute as darkness is falling. Be comfortable, be rested, be ready and refreshed to start the next day. It is better to stop earlier than late, and to have a good meal and a long sleep. The obvious places *not* to camp are near potential rock falls, by a stream likely to overflow if it rains, or where the ground may become waterlogged. Hollows and the bottoms of steep valleys are bad spots because colder, denser air sinks down into them. A level patch of ground higher up will be better, particularly if it faces the morning sun and is backed by a natural windbreak. Keep out of fields with cattle in them; on open fells and moorland they will not feel threatened and are unlikely to be a problem provided they are ignored. Marsh, bog, brackish water and sometimes bracken are great breeding grounds for insects which can make a camp site untenable. On high ground a stone wall can be a good windbreak, and where there are no walls there will usually be plenty of stones and boulders with which to build one, even if it is just small enough for a cooking area. A wind-blown flame never brings water to the boil!

In winter forests are the best sites as they provide good

shelter, with conifers being better than deciduous trees since pine and spruce grow on well drained soil. However, care must be taken not to site tents under heavily snow-laden trees as tents have been flattened by snow falling off them, branches included sometimes. In strong winds and drifting snow open areas should be avoided, but if there is nowhere else, seek shelter in the lee of what natural windbreaks can be found—in depressions or behind pressure ridges of ice on lakes and glaciers; a strong overhead wind may, with luck, create a still area on the lee side of a slope. In the open, high winds will rapidly deposit snow on the weather side of any obstruction. If an obstruction can be made with branches or saplings bent over and tied down, a thick wall of solid snow will soon build up against them. With firm snow, blocks can be cut to build a wall, or a hole dug big enough to pitch the tent in, with the excavated snow used to form a windbreak.

Never site a tent below a snow cornice or at the foot of any snow slope that could form a potential avalanche. These tend to occur in the same place year after year, and in the treeline their paths are recognisable by the swathes they have previously cut, ripping off branches and sometimes leaving only stumps. Large mountain areas create their own micro-climates that often do not relate to the weather pattern for the surrounding countryside. So, when camping in the mountains, it must be assumed that there may be a storm before the day is out, whatever the general weather forecast. Before retiring for the night everything should be left ready for the morning—kit to be put on, water for the brew-up, food for breakfast and the cooker fuelled then, if conditions outside are bad, everything can be done without leaving the tent.

Great care must be exercised when cooking inside a tent. A paraffin cooker should only be re-fuelled when it is cold and, when a stove is burning, the tent should be well ventilated to prevent a build-up of toxic gases. Normal leaded petrol in cookers or lamps in a tent or shelter is dangerous to health. Use de-leaded petrol, called Naptha, or white petrol. Solid fuel (Hexamine) must never *ever* be used inside a tent. Tent eye is irritation of the eyes by fumes from cookers, heaters, lamps and cigarette smoke in badly ventilated tents and shelters. The eyes water and become red and painful. The only treatment is to move into fresh air and to resist rubbing the eyes, which will only make them worse. Some tents have a flap in the groundsheet which can be raised so that the cooker sits on the ground, and if there is a flare-up the groundsheet will not catch fire. By far the safest method if you must cook inside the tent is to do so by the entrance with the zip open so that, in the event of an accident, the cooker can be quickly thrown outside.

CHAPTER 7

SAFELY THERE AND BACK

Navigation — the use of map and compass to know where you are all the time — is the first skill of fieldcraft. For some people it is a competitive sport in its own right, called orienteering. But even when used as an aid to getting you safely there and back in difficult country, it can engender a sense of achievement. Having confidence in your position leaves the mind free to observe and enjoy the scenery and the nature of it, and it offers the peace of mind needed for good forward planning. On the other hand, uncertainty about where you are, the fear of being lost and benighted, and worrying about how to get back, will take all the fun out of what you are doing and can turn an enjoyable adventure into a nightmare. There can be no doubt that the prime cause of many walking and climbing disasters was someone getting lost. No one would wander in circles until they became exhausted had they known where they were in the first place and which was the way home. Likewise, no one would fall down a gulley in mist if they knew where *it* was and where *they* were when the mist came down. Most certainly the ability to navigate accurately over difficult terrain and in poor visibility is an invaluable survival skill, sometimes the only one needed to save life.

It is the height of folly to stray far from the beaten track or to tackle any crosscountry walk without a good topographical map. Landranger maps published by the Ordnance Survey cover Great Britain in 204 sheets. With a scale of 1:50,000 (1·25in to 1 mile, or 2cm to 1 km) they are suitable both as motoring and off-road maps. The walker and climber who needs to know his position to within 100m (109yd) will probably use 1:25,000 maps (the Pathfinder Series). With their large scale of 2·5in to 1 mile (4cm to 1 km) they show every feature, natural or man-made, existing at the time of publication, that could be of practical use. The tiniest stream can be followed and, with contours at 25ft vertical intervals (now being replaced by metric contours at 10m intervals), the shape of the blandest landscape can be identified.

These maps normally cover an area of 20km x 20km (about 150 sq miles) with variations among the coastal ones. More economical, but larger and more awkward to handle in the field, are the Outdoor Leisure Maps (also 1:25,000), which cover popular areas like Dartmoor, the Brecon Beacons, Snowdonia and the Cairngorms. They carry a lot more tourist information, including youth hostels, camping and caravan sites, and viewpoints. The grid lines, N/S and E/W, on the 1:25,000 scale maps conveniently represent distances of 1 km (1,094yd). They are printed at 4cm intervals, which makes each centimetre on the map equal to 250m on the ground (or, roughly, each 1½ in interval equals 273½ yd).

To define a point on the map accurately to within 100m (109yd), each grid square has to be divided into 100 x 100m squares by dividing each grid line into tenths. First take the west edge of the grid square in which your point lies and read the figure for that grid line on the north or south margin of the map, which is, let us say, 60. Then divide the distance from that N/S grid line to the next grid line eastwards (to the right) into tenths and estimate which tenth line runs through or nearest to your point. If it is half way across the square it will be 5/10ths. Therefore you have a 3-figure grid reference of 605 easting. You now want a northing grid reference, so read the figure for the grid that runs along the south edge of your grid square, which is, say, 20. Then divide the distance from that E/W grid line to the next one to the north (up) into tenths and estimate which one-tenth line runs through or nearest to your point. If it is two tenths up from the bottom of the grid square you will have a 3-figure grid reference of 202 northing. Put the two together and you have a grid reference accurate to within 100m (109yd) of 605202. If working on more than one map it will be necessary to prefix your grid reference number with the two grid letters for the map or part of the map you are using. Your 6-figure grid reference actually recurs at intervals of 100km (62½ miles) throughout the entire series. The OS grid numbers must not be confused with degrees of longitude and

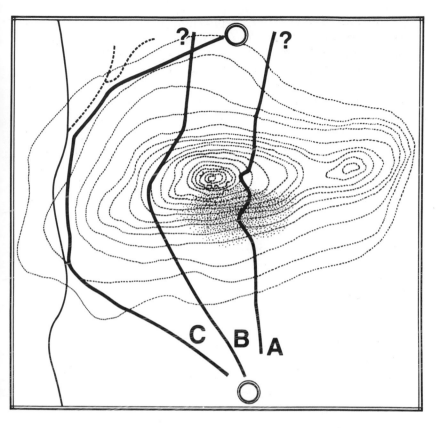

Fig 8   Routes across contour lines to illustrate that the shortest route is not always the best:
Route A: the straight line route may be shorter in horizontal distance, but steep climbs and rough terrain will often mean a very much longer journey in time
Route B: this route has no guiding features and some fairly steep gradients
Route C: the simplest, safest and probably the fastest route especially as there is a path and fairly flat terrain

latitude, which are on a totally different and larger scale.

All the information you are likely to want is available on an OS map if you know how to read it. Study the legend on a few maps at home until you are familiar with the signs, symbols and colours so that you know the difference between a county boundary and a line of electricity pylons, railways and footpaths and, of course, between public conveniences and public houses. Contour lines, which join together all points of the same height, with spot heights marked on summits, show the shape of the landscape if you can visualise it in three dimensions. One way of doing that is to draw a line through a number of contours crossing at least a valley and a couple of hills and make a graph of the varying heights. This will give you some impression of the relative steepness of gradients and show up false horizons that would restrict your view at ground level compared with the 'aerial' one you get looking down on a map. Then make a similar graph of the contour heights along the length of a marked footpath. This will almost certainly show much gentler gradients, because tracks tend to follow contour lines round the base of steep ground as far as they can to give man and beast an easier and safer journey.

Sheep tracks are excellent examples of how to cross high ground comfortably and with the minimum of effort. So emulate the sheep; choose two points on a map away from any marked paths and separated by steep and broken ground. Using the contour lines and other markings shown work out a route between your two points which has easy gradients and the most level ground to walk on without going too far out of your way. Although longer than the direct route, it will almost certainly be quicker and less tiring in the end.

The following short notes on the types of terrain that can be encountered in open country will help in practising route planning off a map. But it takes practical experience to become good at choosing suitable and imaginative routes.

1   Short grass is easy to move across; long and deep grass is tiring and upsets rhythm. Grass coated in ice or thin snow is very slippery and should be crossed with care. Lightweight rock climbing (and some walking) boots are particularly slippery on wet grass, so care must be taken at the tops of climbs when wearing them.

2   Bogs, which are frequently found in European hill and mountain areas, should be avoided if possible as they will soak the feet and delay movement. In some parts they can be deep and treacherous.

3 Bracken is normally deep and thick, consequently hiding boulders and potholes, so it should be avoided when possible.

4 Heather covered slopes are normally fairly easily crossed because the plant is tough. Nevertheless, in areas where it is deep and thick progress can be slow and tiring.

5 Scree is the term used to describe a slope covered in loose stones which should be avoided in ascent. In descent such slopes can provide a quick and easy route if the stones are small and there are no cliffs or minor drops on the way. Individuals can run down the slope with knees bent and heels digging in. Groups should go down sticking close together in line abreast as there is a danger of large stones being dislodged, which might cause injury to anyone ahead.

6 On any slope or steep face loose stones are often encountered, so care must be taken not to dislodge them. In the event of a dislodgement the word 'Below' should be shouted to warn others.

Recruits on the 30-mile march

7   Steep rock slabs should be avoided because of the difficulty in retaining balance when crossing them.

8   Rivers more often than not have to be considered as barriers forcing detours to be made. The techniques of crossing rivers are dealt with at the end of this chapter.

Having planned a few routes for imaginary walks, you can start estimating how long they would take travelling light with a day sack and then heavily laden with camping, climbing and survival gear. To get reasonable and achievable estimates for crossing rough hill country, apply the timings used by the Royal Marines to move men across mountainous terrain. For lightly equipped men they allow one hour for every 5km (3 miles) measured on the map plus an additional hour for every 600m (2,000ft) gained in height, and pro rata. When heavily laden, the time allowance is measured to between 2·5km (1½ miles) and 4km (2½ miles) an hour depending on load and gradients plus an additional hour for every 470m (1,500ft) gained in height. Always add 10 minutes' rest time in every hour to your calculations. Incidentally, in Commando terms, heavy loads start at about 22·7kg (50lb) for which they recommend a 5 minute rest every half hour.

Both when planning a route and when actually walking, it is important to remember that pace and rhythm are essential to conserve energy. This becomes more important on high ground. Start a walk at a slow and comfortable pace and work up to a faster one that can be maintained. Only stop at prearranged points, as frequent halts or indecision about halts will break the rhythm. The route may be planned for many miles ahead, but each individual should be concentrating on the next few metres ahead — in other words, do not let your attention wander so that you trip over a boulder or twist your ankle in a hole. When traversing steep ground, use flat turfs or stones when you can to relieve the ankles of constant sideways placement and strain. Go up steep slopes in a gentle zigzag, like sheep do, rather than going hell-bent straight up to the summit.

Having blazed trails across your kitchen table you should be familiar with all the Ordnance Survey markings, and the time has come to take a map out into the countryside and, from a

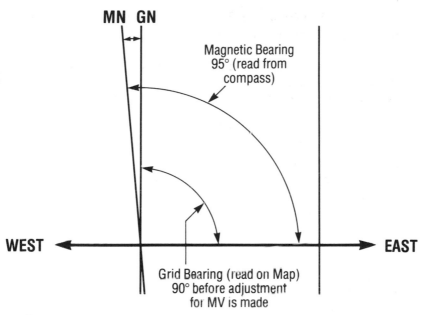

Fig 9   Magnetic and grid bearing diagram

high viewpoint, identify on the map what you see on the ground, and vice versa. To do this properly the map has to be orientated so that north on it points to north on the ground. You may be able to do this by lining the map up with a straight road or row of pylons, but the conventional way is to line up a vertical grid line with the compass needle, the top of the grid facing north of course. The grid lines will then be pointing to magnetic north, not true north. The variation is of little consequence for rough and ready map reading, but has to be taken into account for precise navigating.

Over centuries magnetic north moves very slowly to and fro east and west of true north, and the variation or angle between magnetic and true also varies slightly according to where you are or, in this context, on which map you are working. Currently magnetic north is west of true north but moving eastwards at about half a degree in 3 years, so the variation (angle) is decreasing. All OS maps give the magnetic variation for the date they were published together with the annual change so, unless the map is very old, it only takes a moment to

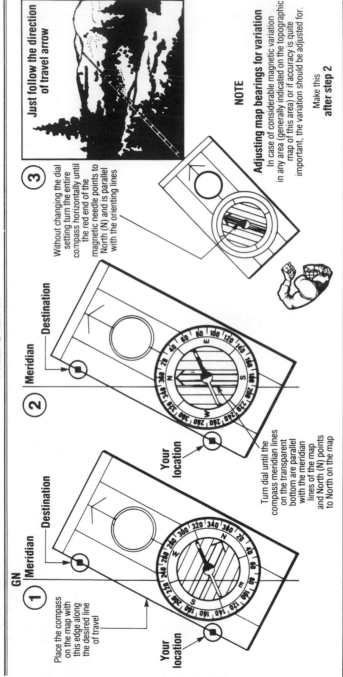

Fig 10 Silva instructions

do the update. For example, the English Lakes 1:25,000 map says that magnetic north was about 6° west of grid north in 1986, decreasing by about half a degree in 3 years. For the pedantic it also says that true north is 1° east of grid north. So in 1990 the variation will be down to about 5° 30′ west.

For magnetic north one can say compass north, and that magnetic bearings are compass bearings. Bearings on a map, on the other hand, are true or grid bearings. If a grid bearing laid on a map was 90° (due east) and the current variation was 5° west you would have to walk on a compass bearing of 95° for it to be along the same line as the one on the map. The 5° are added to make up for the magnetic reading being 5° west of, that is *less* than, the grid bearing. Working the other way round, when a compass bearing of 90° has to be drawn on a map the 5° variation would have to be subtracted to give a grid bearing of 85° because the grid north is 5° east of (more than) magnetic north. Only over very short distances can those few degrees of variation be ignored — a 5° error in 1km is 100m (176yd in 1 mile) but after 10km it becomes 1km (1 mile in 10 miles) which, in some terrain, would be enough to get you completely lost. If at this stage there is any confusion over the word 'bearing', think of the word 'angle' as used in geometry and imagine a map overlaid with a 360° protractor; 360/0 would be north, 90 would be east, 180 south and 270 west.

Map and compass should be inseparable companions, but while not every member of a group will always carry a map, a compass is a very personal tool without which one should never go off the beaten track. If you have only a map it is difficult to orientate yourself, to decide on the direction to walk and to keep to it. With a compass you always know in which direction you are going, and you can take bearings off features to keep a check on your position. It is a most comforting friend because it will always show you the way in mist or in darkness—there are even Braille and audio versions that will lead the blind. Always remember that, left without anything to guide us, our natural tendency is to walk in a continuing curve to left or right. Given time, it might end up as a complete circle so that you return to where you started. It is generally agreed that the most useful all-purpose compass is the orienteering type which incorporates a protractor with a direction-of-travel arrow on it and a rotating bezel marked in degrees round the compass card.

The Silva system of compasses is widely acknowledged as the best of this type, and they are standard NATO and Commando issue. The following instructions published by Silva on the use of their compasses are concise little lessons in map reading and direction finding in their own right:

'1. Place compass on map with one edge along the desired line of travel.

2. Rotate the dial until the compass's meridian (grid) lines on the transparent bottom are parallel with the meridian (grid) lines on the map and North (N) points to North on the map.

3. Without changing the dial setting turn the entire compass horizontally until the red end of the magnetic needle points to North (N) on the compass dial and is parallel with the orienting lines (the meridian or grid lines). Then just follow the direction of the big travel arrow on the base plate. Choose a landmark or spot in this direction and walk to it without looking at the compass. Then choose a new landmark and repeat the process until you reach your destination.'

(Some Sylva compasses combine optical or mirror sighting for taking bearings at eye level with the protractor facility.)

'If the magnetic variation is large or great accuracy is important the adjustment for variation should be made after step 2 above. For example if variation is 10 degrees West, turn dial West 10 degrees (ADD). If the variation is shown as 10 degrees East turn dial East 10 degrees (SUBTRACT).'

One type of Silva compass is fitted with a simple device for setting a 'permanent' allowance for variation. To plot your position on the map you need to take bearings with your compass on two or more features, which you can see on the ground and which you can identify on the map; a summit, a building, or the edge of a wood are examples. Having noted the compass bearing, convert it to a back bearing, to its reciprocal.

Between 0° and 180° you add 180°, and between 181° and 360° you subtract 180° so 90° becomes 270°, and 300° becomes 120°. Then convert your back bearing from magnetic to grid and plot it on the map. Where two back bearings from two features meet on the map should be very near where you are. If a third bearing is taken, all three should meet at the exact point, but this is an imperfect world and you will be lucky if you do better than get a very small triangle on the map. Your position is inside it. Choose features that are as near 90° apart as possible to get the most accurate results.

With only a little practice it will be unnecessary most times to transpose bearings onto the map. You will be able to take your bearings and visualise where they would meet on the map. With a 1:25,000 scale there will be so much detail corresponding to what you see around you that bearings will often only confirm what you have already guessed your position to be. When there are no two features at a suitable angle apart to give good cross bearings, look for two features that are exactly one behind the other — in transit — or so near together that a short walk will bring them in transit. Draw a line through the two features on the map extended in your direction (back bearing again) and you will be somewhere along that line. A sense of distance, the character of the ground around you, or an approximate second bearing taken from the position of the sun will help to establish your position on that line.

When marching on a fixed bearing it should not be necessary to keep checking with the compass, which will slow you down and interrupt the rhythm of your walking. Instead, find an object or feature in the distance that is on the same bearing as you want to march on. If you are lucky it will be a big tree, rock outcrop or peak. More likely you will have to settle for a splodge of colour on the ground or a small nick in the contour of a hill. Whatever it is, walk towards it until it is hidden by a false horizon, the perspective changes its shape out of recognition, or you reach it. Then take another bearing on another point and walk towards that.

In featureless landscapes, or in poor visibility, two or more people can provide their own marks by walking in single file at some distance apart with the one behind taking bearings on the leader. To be more accurate, but at a very much slower pace, they can leap-frog, with the person in front standing still while the one behind comes up to him. This is a good method of keeping direction at night with the rear person taking bearings on the leader's torch. It is no good setting off on a bearing with no target in front of you, and then not looking at your compass for a mile or two, because you will almost certainly have walked in a curve, and although your compass will give you your bearing again it will not tell you by how much you have wandered off your correct track. When there is nothing ahead to aim for, it may sometimes be possible to check that you are keeping in a straight line by taking back bearings on a feature behind you. In snow or sand you can tell if you are walking straight, and on what bearing, by looking back along your tracks. If they are reasonably straight, you can double-check by taking a bearing on them, which should be the reciprocal of the one you have to march on.

Compasses can, of course, malfunction in proximity to stray magnetic fields that compete with the weaker one of the earth. Such fields exist around electrical circuits in cars, aeroplanes and generators; and almost any mass of metal may affect the polarity of the compass needle. Check your compass like every other item of equipment before going out in the field. The polarity of the needle can be improved (or restored if it has changed) by stroking the south pole of a strong magnet along the north end of the needle. There are odd places all over the world where a compass will go haywire because of the amount of magnetic iron ore in the ground. This problem is most likely to be met in mountains, and is part of the local knowledge to be picked up when going to a new location for the first time. Compasses will also behave sluggishly, or show random deviation, in many parts of the Arctic. The earth's magnetic field is weaker there, and rather than flowing straight up north it dips into the ground — understandable when you look at a globe — and the needle tries to dip down to follow it and may stick on its pivot. If this is suspected, watch the needle swinging and take a mean reading, not the one where the needle stops.

The pocket altimeter is the third navigational tool that can be used together with map and compass in the mountains to establish position. It is used during ascents and descents (when it shows height changes, which can be related to the map contour lines) and on summits and spot heights when altitude readings can be checked with those on the map. It is most useful in reduced visibility when, by keeping track of your compass directions and changes in height, it should be possible to plot fairly accurately the route taken and, therefore, where you are. It does not actually measure height but atmospheric pressure and is therefore a barometer, but it is calibrated in metres. Pressure decreasing with height is shown as an increase in altitude, and pressure increasing with height loss is shown as a decrease in altitude. Because the actual barometric pressure changes according to the weather as well as altitude, the height shown on the altimeter must be related to the height (pressure) shown at the start of a climb or descent. After approximately 300m of ascent or descent, or after about an hour of travelling, the altimeter should be recalibrated in case a change in the weather (barometric pressure) has falsified the height reading. This is best done on arrival at a known point and height on the map. The altimeter will also work as a barometer to give warning of deteriorating weather or the good news of it clearing up. But for accurate measurement of barometric pressure for weather forecasting it is necessary to remain in one place or at one altitude for 3 to 4 hours.

A golden rule, which is rather more honoured in the breach than in the observance, is that nobody should go on an expedition without first making out a route card to take with him and leaving behind a copy for a potential rescue team should he become overdue. For a long trek into rough country, possibly with natural obstacles to be got round, it can involve a lot of hard work, but it has several very practical uses and, in extremis, could be vital to survival. First and foremost it forces an individual, or party leader, to take a long and detailed look at the map along the whole of a proposed route and, presumably, foresee any problems that might be met with. It concentrates the mind on the task and has the salutary effect of dampening down excess zeal and over-ambition. It is the only reliable way of estimating the time that will be taken, which must affect the amount of food, drink, clothing and survival gear to be carried. If the worst happens, those estimates will be invaluable to a search party.

Accurate timings can only be estimated after considering

how the recent weather may have affected underfoot conditions, the current weather pattern, the fitness, stamina and experience of the individuals, and allowing for the likely pace of the slowest or weakest member of the party. If making a route card sounds like hard work, remember that it is easier to work out accurate bearings at home with a map on the table than on a mountainside in a gale. The route should be divided into convenient or natural legs, and the start and finish of each filled in with a description or name, grid reference and the magnetic bearing. The terrain along each leg ought to be described sufficiently well for it to be navigated in poor visibility. More details are needed for difficult or featureless country than when following marked ways. Make a note of potential dangers such as scree, convex slopes and bog. Some legs will, perforce, be dog legs with two or more bearings, and then the distance will have to be split. Height gained on any leg has to be calculated into the estimated time. The quickest way of doing this is to count the number of contour lines crossed on an uphill section and multiply that number by 50ft, 25ft, 10m or whatever vertical interval applies on the map being used. Time should not be deducted for going downhill because a steady pace should be maintained — running headlong downhill can be dangerous — and in fact time may have to be added for steep and awkward descents.

Naismith's Rule is the one universally used for estimating time and distance, and is the basis of the Commandos' estimates for moving lightly equipped men. His rule for day walks is: 5km (3 miles) per hr + 30min for every 300m (985ft) ascent. Therefore 100m (330ft) = 1·2min and 1km = 12min (1 mile = 20min) and 10m of ascent (1 metric contour) = plus 1min, and 600m of ascent = plus 1 hr. On the OS 1:25,000 scale maps with contours at 10m vertical intervals you can allow 1 minute for each contour line crossed (for the 25ft contour, allow 45 seconds for each contour line). The following information, which will help a search party, must be on the back of the route card left at base or your departure point:

Name of individual, or leader of party.
Details of party (ages, experience, equipment carried, etc).

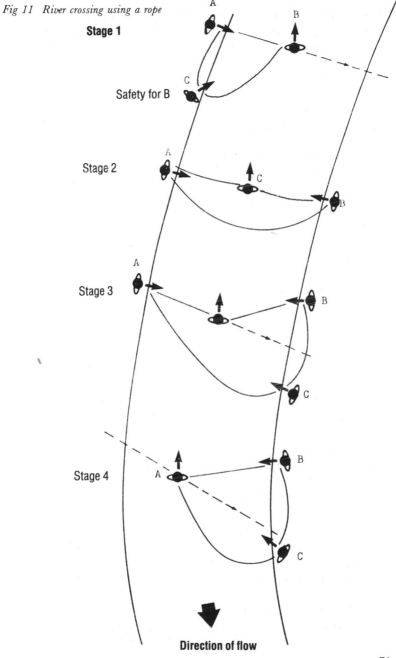

Fig 11 River crossing using a rope

Stage 1

A

B

Safety for B

C

Stage 2

A

C

B

Stage 3

A

B

C

Stage 4

A

B

C

Direction of flow

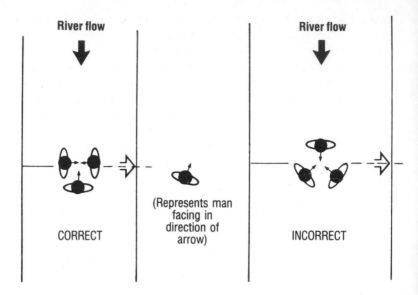

Fig 12 River crossing

Departure time.

Estimated time of return.

Escape routes (ie diversions from planned route that will be made if the walk/climb has to be curtailed or abandoned for any reason, the most likely being weather). The route card should be kept in a waterproof map case, plastic bag or be covered with Fablon.

A river may look like an innocent thin blue line on the map, but after heavy rain it could be a dangerous and impassable barrier. So be most circumspect about planning a route across streams and rivers in winter. Only if it is more hazardous to take a route up- or down-stream would a crossing in those circumstances be warranted, and then the water must be clearly fordable and great care taken to determine that it is. If a foothold is lost in fast moving boulder-strewn water, the consequences can be horrible. When there is any doubt, or apparent danger, a safety rope should be used. If you have to make a crossing, give time to selecting the best crossing point. Deep water flows slower than shallow, although that does not mean that it is better to go in up to your neck if you can find an ankle-deep crossing. Bends are suspect as the water may have cut a deep channel on the outside curve.

Look for easy access and exit points, particularly the latter—after a cold and exhausting crossing, a steep and slippery bank might be just too much in waterlogged clothing. Always keep your boots on; a stubbed toe or cut foot will make walking agony. When testing the force of the water use a rope belayed to a fixed point or to a companion, and a stick, both for support and to prod for depth. Avoid the temptation of leaping from boulder to boulder if there is any risk of slipping and being injured or falling in. If on your own, face upstream and shuffle your feet sideways taking a course of 45° to the flow of the water.

The Tyrolean Traverse is the simplest way of using a rope, if good fixing points are available on both sides of the water and one person is capable and strong enough to take it, and a running line, across. Other members of the party and their loads can then hang on to the fixed line and be pulled over by the running line. Ideally, the person being pulled across would be attached to the fixed line by a sling, with the running line around his waist. With a sufficiently long loop of rope, three people can support each other for a crossing using the tactic shown in Fig 11. For more than three people, just substitute a queue for the single body of A. Without rope, groups of three people can help each other across by forming a human tripod in the water. With heads close together, arms firmly linked and feet apart, they move crabwise across, one man shuffling at a time while the other two are in support; the lower of the three faces upstream all the time (see Fig 12).

CHAPTER 8

SURVIVAL NAVIGATION

Survival navigation is one of the many skills Commandos must learn on the assumption that, if they were ever captured, they would have to escape without assistance of map or compass. For the civilian there can rarely be any excuse for being lost without those aids, but the plain truth is that people do go out without them and get lost. What is more common is for one or more persons to lose touch with the rest of a party that is being led by the only person with a map. However, even in the best organised communities, things can go wrong and equipment, including those two vital navigational tools, may be lost by some act of God or carelessness. Survival may then depend on someone being able to find the way using the sun, moon, stars or other signs and phenomena of nature to navigate by.

Everyone knows that the sun rises in the east and sets in the west, and that anywhere in the northern hemisphere it is due south at midday and, conversely, in the southern hemisphere it is due north at midday. That is only a very general rule. The sun in the northern hemisphere rises in the south-east in January and then further north each day until by midsummer's day, 24 June, it rises in the north-east. Similarly, it sets in the south-west in January and the north-west at midsummer. By observing where the sun rises and sets it is possible to estimate where true north lies. This azimuth table for the rising and setting sun for latitude 50° north to 60° north covers the whole of the British Isles except for some of the Shetland Isles.

For the rising sun, the azimuth (bearing) is reckoned from the north to east, and for the setting sun from north to west. To find north from the rising sun if you were in Gretna Green on 16 April you would follow the 55 column (Gretna Green is conveniently on latitude 55°N) down to 16 April and read off

Royal Marines of the Raiding Squadron in a rigid raider

the figure 72. That morning the sun rises 72° east of true north. In other words, north will be 72° to your left when you face the rising sun. At sunset, north will be 72° to your right when you face the setting sun. For an accuracy of one degree it would be necessary to interpolate between the figures given in the abridged table above. But, by using the nearest latitude to the one you are on and the nearest day listed, the bearing given will be good enough for most situations. To be able to use the information from the azimuth table to locate north, it is necessary to know how many degrees are covered by one or more of your fingers, or by your palm width, or your out-stretched fingers when held at arm's length, or have some other method of measuring degrees without a compass.

An azimuth table could be put to many uses. For example, once you know the times and azimuth of sunrise and sunset for a particular day, and the fact that the sun moves east to west at 15° per hour, it is possible, without a compass, to work out the

Latitude			Date	
50	55	60		
127	133	141	1	January
127	132	140	6	
125	130	138	11	
124	129	136	16	
122	127	133	21	
120	124	130	26	
117	121	126	1	February
115	118	123	6	
112	116	120	11	
110	112	116	16	
107	109	112	21	
104	106	108	26	
102	104	106	1	March
99	100	102	6	
96	97	98	11	
93	93	94	16	
90	90	90	21	
87	87	86	26	
83	82	81	1	April
80	79	77	6	
77	76	74	11	
74	72	70	16	
72	69	66	21	
69	66	63	26	
66	63	59	1	May
64	61	56	6	
62	58	52	11	
60	55	49	16	
58	53	47	21	
56	51	44	26	
54	49	41	1	June
53	48	40	6	
53	47	39	11	
53	47	39	16	
53	47	39	.21	
53	47	39	26	

| Latitude | | | Date | |
50	55	60		
53	47	39	1	
53	48	40	6	
54	49	41	11	July
55	50	43	16	
57	52	45	21	
59	54	48	26	
61	57	51	1	
63	60	55	6	
66	63	58	11	August
68	65	61	16	
71	68	65	21	
73	71	68	26	
77	75	73	1	
80	78	77	6	
83	82	81	11	September
85	85	84	16	
88	88	88	21	
92	92	92	26	
95	95	96	1	
98	99	100	6	
101	102	104	11	October
104	105	108	16	
107	109	112	21	
109	112	115	26	
113	116	120	1	
115	119	123	6	
117	121	126	11	November
120	124	130	16	
122	126	133	21	
124	128	135	26	
125	130	138	1	
126	132	140	6	
127	133	141	11	December
127	133	141	16	
127	133	141	21	
127	133	141	26	

bearing of the sun by the time or, conversely, if you have a compass but no watch, the correct time by taking a bearing on the sun. An accurate watch will always tell you when it is midday, and the sun where south is. It does not matter if it is a digital or analogue watch, but the latter is more useful because it can be used as a compass throughout daylight hours if the sun is visible. Using a watch is one of the best known methods of finding north and south although, except at midday, it should be accepted as a rough guide only. To do this, in the northern hemisphere, hold the watch parallel to the ground and turn it so that the hour hand is pointing at the sun. True south will then lie midway between the hour hand and 12 o'clock on the watch face. The same line extended the other way obviously points to the north. In the southern hemisphere, the watch is turned so that a line from the centre through the 12 figure points at the sun. Then a line extended from the centre of the watch through a point midway between 12 o'clock and the hour hand will point to true north.

In any latitude, and at any time during the day, an accurate east/west line can be marked on the ground using the following method: Push a stick or something similar into the ground in a flat clear area. Mark the tip of the shadow thrown on the ground. Wait exactly 10 minutes, and again mark the tip of the shadow on the ground. A straight line joining the two marks will run due west/east from the first to the second mark. A variation of the stick and shadow technique can be used to find the north/south line at midday. The stick must be stuck in the ground and the tip of its shadow marked before midday. Using a length of string, a belt, or whatever is available, describe an arc on the ground from the base of the stick the same radius as the length of the shadow. When the shadow touches the arc again after midday, mark that position and then bisect the angle formed by the base of the stick and the two marks. The line bisecting the angle will indicate south in the northern hemisphere, and north in the southern hemisphere. Time can be saved by watching the shadow and marking its position as it gets shorter. At the moment when it is at its shortest, or shrinks furthest away from the arc, it will be pointing south. If the shadow does not shrink before growing longer then it is too late — you have missed the noon deadline. All these methods depend on the sun being visible. When there is too much cloud cover, mist or fog other ways, akin to primitive field craft, have to be used.

The North American Indians were known to be natural navigators in their forests and across the vast prairies of their sparsely inhabited continent. The courses of rivers provided them with obvious directional grids, and they were adept at using the sun and stars, but when neither was visible they used trees as compasses. The bark, they knew, was dull and darker on the north-facing trunk and healthier looking on the south-facing side. If that difference was not too clear, they would cut into the tree with an axe and inspect the rings, which would be thicker on the north side and thinner, or closer together, on the south side.

Cutting into trees is not acceptable behaviour in most countries today, but in an emergency social behaviour and environmental regard might have to be ignored for once. On the other hand, where there are woods or copses there may be a few tree stumps whose rings can be studied. In many of the highland areas of Great Britain the alien forestry plantations often provide an abundance of tree stumps. Plants always grow towards the sun — that is in a southerly direction in the northern hemisphere — and foliage on trees and bushes, which will be most abundant on the sunny side, are other good indicators of direction. As the sun affects plant growth (hence the north/south aspect of tree rings) so also does the wind, which tends to make all plants bend away from its prevailing onslaught, particularly so on open terrain. Therefore, if you know the direction of the prevailing wind, which is SW in most parts of Britain, you can assume that when trees and tall grasses in the open are seen to bend or lean it will probabaly be towards the north-west away from the wind.

But beware of taking that assumption for gospel — there are many cases where valleys, the lees of hills and escarpments, can cancel out or deflect the direction of the prevailing wind. Such exceptions to rules are good reasons for doing your homework and, if possible, seeking local knowledge about any new area in which you will be operating. The effect of the wind on grass and other low plants is not so obvious as with trees, hedgerows and cereals. With fairly short grasses and tufts it

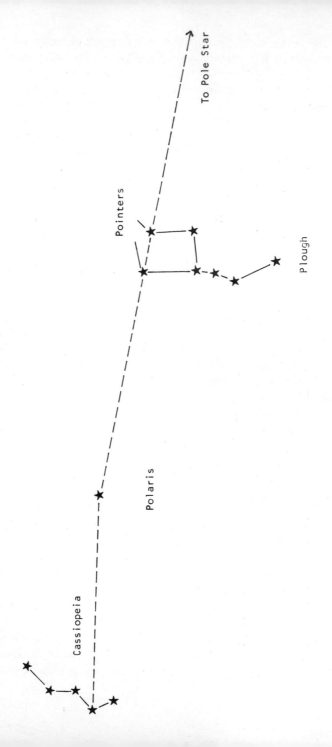

Fig 13 Finding true North or the Pole Star by stars in the Northern hemisphere

may be possible to check with a hand which way they are tending to grow by feeling in which direction they offer the most resistance to hand pressure. In sandy areas sand-tailings behind trees and plants are also tell-tales of the prevailing wind direction, and sand dunes themselves slope gently on their windward side and fall away steeply on their lee side. The prevailing wind effect can, of course, be wiped out by a hard or long blow from an unusual direction, say a northerly gale in winter.

Like any field craft, natural methods of navigation require a lot of practice before one can rely on them, and that applies most particularly to navigating at night. In the dark our senses play us false and we tend to become apprehensive, if not fearful. It is then that confidence is most needed. Everyone knows that the North Star—the Pole Star or Polaris, whatever name you use — is always in the north in the northern hemisphere, but it starts to lose its usefulness above 60° latitude when it goes too high in the sky to be a good guide; at the North Pole it is vertically overhead. The fact that it fluctuates about 2° is neither here nor there to the survival navigator. What is important is to be able to find it quickly, because very often there will be cloud about and it may only appear intermittently; the same can, of course, be said of any heavenly observations at night.

The position of the North Star is found by following the line of the 'pointers' of the Great Bear (Ursa Major) or the Big Dipper or the Plough as it is more commonly called. It is that group of seven stars that looks a little bit like a plough, but is more like a saucepan with a curved handle. The two stars forming the side of the pan furthest from the handle point to the North Star. Extend a line through those two stars (from the bottom of the pan to the lip, that is) about five times and it will hit the North Star, which is in a group called the Little Bear and looks like a square kite with four stars in its tail. The North Star shines brightly at the end of the tail. Do not expect the Plough to always look like a plough or a saucepan because, like all stars, this group revolves around the North or Pole Star and may appear to be standing on its end or upside down. It is the right way up when it is below the North Star, and upside down when it is above it. If it should be obscured by cloud or horizon, another group of five stars called Cassiopeia, shaped like a flattened out W, can be used as a pointer. This group will always be positioned at approximately 180° to the Plough and on the far side of, but slightly closer to, the North Star through which a line bisecting the right V of the W would pass.

In the southern hemisphere the Southern Cross has the opposite function of establishing the position of the South Pole, although it is not as accurate as it may be offset from true south. Again this four-star group can be likened to a diamond-shaped kite, and a straight line bisecting the diamond and extended earthwards like a kite's tail will touch the horizon at a point that is approximately true south. There is a false cross to the west and below the Southern Cross, but the true cross can be checked by the two bright stars side by side slightly below and to the east of it.

Stars appear to move in an arc from east to west but, in fact, it is the earth that revolves below them. However, this illusion is a useful guide to direction. Arrange two fixed points — two stakes stuck in the ground or a large forked stick — to be used like the open sights of a rifle through which to watch a star, any star. In the course of a few minutes it will either rise over, move left or right of, or drop below, the sights. If it rises, you are facing approximately east. If it falls, you are facing approximately west. If it curves to the right, you are facing approximately south. If it curves to the left, you are facing approximately north.

The constellation of Orion lies over the celestial equator and in its centre are three stars, called the Belt of Orion, close together in a diagonal line. The highest star of the three is exactly on the celestial equator and, wherever on earth you may be, that star will always rise due east of you and set due west. The moon can be a guide to general direction if it is remembered that the lit side is always facing the sun. Therefore, if the moon rises before the sun has set the illuminated side will be on the west, and when it rises some time after the sun has gone down the illuminated side will be on the east. An imaginary line joining the horns of an incomplete moon extended up and down approximates the north/south line. The following table can be used to ascertain the broad bearing of the moon at certain specific times:

Local Time	When the moon is in its		
	1st Quarter	Full Moon	Last Quarter
1800	south	east	N/A
2100	south-west	south-east	N/A
Midnight	west	south	east
0300	N/A	south-west	south-east
0600	N/A	west	south

A spin-off from learning to obtain bearings from the sun and stars is that they can be used to check on your compass and update the magnetic variations on your maps; if the maps are fairly old, the variations may be great enough to cause serious errors in your navigation. To check your compass, take a sight on the heavenly body being used as a reference and note its magnetic bearing. The difference between that magnetic bearing and the true bearing of the body will be the variation of your position. If using an up-to-date map you can check if the variation is in part the fault of the compass. Providing the compass is accurate, it will show the current variation for the area you are in and that can be marked on an old map to bring it up-to-date. For example, the true bearing of the sun at midday is 180°, so if the magnetic bearing reads 190° the variation is 10°W and that figure must be subtracted from your magnetic bearings to get true bearings. If the difference is very small, say 2° or 3°, make another check before marking your map. Even modest variations can become large errors over a distance of a day's march. Come nightfall you could be 2km or more than a mile from where you wanted to be — a nuisance at any time, and very serious in bad visibility and hostile weather.

CHAPTER 9

SAFETY ON
THE HIGH GROUND

The following safety advice applies to all activities in mountainous areas, which are defined as open, hilly country and moorland exposed to the elements, where one is self-dependent and remote from any immediate help.

Make sure that there are sufficient hours of daylight to reach your goal, leaving a good margin for delay or poor estimating; never overestimate the stamina of yourself or a party. Remember that weather can change very quickly; it is always worse higher up, and what was easy in summer may be dangerous in winter. Be very cautious and lacking in ambition

Recruit on the Tarzan course

in bad weather. Treat hills with great respect in snow conditions, and keep off snow covered mountains unless you have some snow and ice climbing skills, or at least know how to use an ice axe. Never leave anyone behind; keep together, moving at the pace of the slowest or least experienced. If the weather worsens, or if the route is too hard or too long, turn back. It is nothing to do with being chicken; it is being sensible and possibly saving other people the trouble and risks of having to come to your rescue.

If walking in composition rubber-soled boots remember that they are very slippery in wet grass, on lichened, mossy or greasy rocks, ice or hard snow. On such surfaces there is a lot to be said for putting on a pair of instep crampons. When rock climbing keep together so that any falling rock will not have time to gather momentum before it hits someone; and on scree slopes move in arrow formation or in line abreast. A lot of accidents happen when people are hurrying down off a mountain to get home. Marked paths are the safest, easiest and quickest way, so do not take short cuts. Choose the more gradual side of a mountain, even if it is a long route, rather than scramble down a steep rock side. Walk, do not run, slide or glissade down a slope unless a clear way can be seen right to the bottom with a safe run out. Be prepared for the worst. An unexpected night out in winter without protection can be fatal. Fingers have been lost because rings have jammed in a crack, so remove rings and wrist watches before rock climbing. Always wear a helmet on the rocks. The international distress signal on the mountains is six blasts on a whistle (or similar sound) repeated at minute intervals, or at night six torchlight flashes. The reply is three blasts or flashes at minute intervals.

The first piece of equipment that the walker and scrambler needs when he goes into the hills where there may be poor footholds is a walking rope. This is much lighter than a climbing rope being, ideally, $\frac{7}{8}$ " (7mm) nylon, which has the advantage of stretching up to 40 per cent under strain and acts as a shock absorber on a fall. The most useful length for most rope work, walking or climbing, is 120ft (36·5m). Carried only for emergencies and not for climbing proper, one length to a party is usually sufficient. Before being able to manage rope it is necessary to know the general terms used, so that

instructions given or read can be understood, to know how it is coiled for carrying, and a few of the knots more commonly used in climbing. A *bight* of rope is a 360° bend in which the rope does not cross itself. A *loop* is a bend in a rope in which it does cross over itself. The *standing end* of a rope is that which is anchored or secured to something. The *running end* of a rope is the working or free end. *Lay* is the term given to describe the direction in which yarns and strands of rope are spun in manufacture. To *belay* is to tie oneself to an anchorage.

There are two basic methods of coiling a rope. The ordinary method: lay the rope on the ground or hang it over a rock face so that no kinks or tangles are apparent. Take one end in the left hand and run the right hand along the rope until both arms are outstretched. Bring both hands together letting the rope fall in a loop to form a first coil, which is laid in the open left hand. Repeat the movement along the length of the rope, forming uniform loops, until the whole length is coiled. If the rope starts to twist, apply an opposite twist with the right hand to allow the original twist to run out of the rope. Ropes that have a right hand lay are coiled in a clockwise direction, and those with a left hand lay in an anti-clockwise direction. Kernmantel rope, which has straight filaments surrounded by a woven outer sheath, can be coiled either way. For convenience and speed, you can coil the rope over your knees while sitting on the ground. To secure a coiled rope for carrying take a 30cm (1ft) long bight in the starting end and lay it on top of the coils. Then uncoil the last loop and wrap that length four or five times round all the coils starting at the bottom, open, end of the bight and then pass the last bit through the bight and pull the running (free) end of the bight to lock off the rope.

The Alpine Method: double the rope to form a bight at its centre and, holding the bight in the left hand, coil the double rope as with the ordinary method until nearly 2m (6ft) of it remains uncoiled. Wrap this remaining length round all the coils just below the left hand, leaving enough to form a bight in the running end, which is passed through the coil under the left hand. Then bring the running end round the other way over

Opposite: The last obstacle on the Tarzan course

Fig 14 Some useful knots used in climbing:

1 Reef knot — used to join two ropes of equal diameter

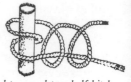

6 Round turn and two half-hitches —
a quick and easy method of
securing a rope to an anchor point

2 Figure-of-eight on the bight — a very efficient and
strong knot which forms a loop which will not
draw tight. Used for belaying

3 Bowline — the commonly used knot to make a
non-slip loop in the end of a rope

4 Bowline on the bight — this knot forms two
non-slip loops and provides a form of bosun's
chair for hauling a person up a cliff/rock face

7 Prussik knot — this is used to ascend
a climbing rope. This knot will
slide freely up or down a rope, but
will grip when weighted. It has many
uses among which are crevasse rescue
and self-help and rescue techniques

5 Triple bowline — this is used as a sit sling (one loop round the waist and
one on each leg), or as a chest harness (one loop under the armpits and the
others over the shoulders) or as a full harness (one loop for each leg and
one across the chest). It is suitable for raising or lowering a person

the top of the coil and through the bight and pull tight to lock off.

As rope is used as a safety line, it should always be inspected before it is taken out. External wear from dragging over rough surfaces, abrasions, cuts and any damage that has severed a strand or partly cut through several, would merit rejection. Rope left lying around on the ground and trodden on will soon pick up a lot of grit and small stones, which get in among the fibres and start cutting them out of sight. Heat will degrade manilla rope without it showing any sign, but it might fail without warning. Nylon rope will soften and 'creep' as it approaches its melting point, which can easily be reached if it is subjected to friction. No ropes like acids or solvents and, if contaminated by any chemical or salt water, they should be soaked for some time in clean water and then dried draped, not coiled.

On slopes where slipping and sliding are the danger, but with little likelihood of vertical falls, it is usually enough to rope up at equal distances along a rope and to keep it just taut enough to steady the next man should he slip. If there is any chance of a member falling and pulling his companion off balance, movement should be one at a time while the other remains belayed — that is secured by a rope round the waist to an anchorage. To tie onto a rope, take one end round your waist twice and tie off in front close to your stomach with a bowline or figure-of-eight on the bight. To belay, the running end is then passed round or over the anchorpoint — rock, tree or ice axe — and brought back and tied with two half hitches to the loops round your waist. The running rope going to the next man is passed through the left hand, under and over the forearm, round the small of the back and through the right hand. (Left-handed people might reverse the procedure). The left hand holds the rope at arm's length and is then pulled back to the body while the right arm is extended, pulling the slack round your back. The left hand is then extended out along the rope and the right hand brought back in to the body. Repeating the process pays the rope out while always keeping it under the control of one hand. By grasping it in both hands at the same time and crossing them in front of your body your back acts as a solid brake. The reverse movements are used to bring the rope in when the other person is descending from above you.

When you are safely belayed, the other person can start moving and, on the way, he can take a turn round any handy projection to provide himself with a running belay which, should he slip and fall, will reduce the distance of the fall. As soon as one person has reached a safe stance he belays himself and brings his companion to him, reversing the roles. The strongest or most experienced person goes first when ascending, but last when descending. The easiest number on a rope is two, and four is the practical maximum.

Communication between people on a rope is important but, if the wind is blowing, words can be snatched away and there can be misunderstandings, especially when two people are shouting out of sight of each other. It is, therefore, best to use the universally accepted system of signals. When a leader is belayed he calls out 'Taking in', and then takes in all the slack. When the second man feels the pull on the rope he shouts, 'That's me'. The leader, if ready, then shouts, 'Climb when ready'. The second man replies, 'Climbing', and, on hearing the leader shout, 'Aye, Aye', starts to do so. If he thinks the rope is too slack for his security he shouts, 'Take in', or, if too taut, 'More slack'.

It is important to realise that walking rope will only take a loading (breaking strain) of 907kg (2,000lb), which may seem a lot but, in fact, is only just enough to save a man on a quite modest fall. A climber weighing 82kg (180lb) falling 30m (82ft) will, when brought up, put an impact force on the rope of 1,038kg (2,288lb). The equivalent rope intended to protect climbers against long vertical falls would be at least 11mm with a breaking strain of 1,900kg (4,200lb). Otherwise use the double rope technique which is now common on the Continent and in this country of two 9mm ropes of different colours.

A more efficient and comfortable method of roping up is to attach the rope to a climbing harness with a karabiner. There are many varieties available, varying from single belt to full body harness. The Royal Marines use the Whillans sit harness. Karabiners are offset oval links that perform much the same functions in climbing as the shackle which attaches a yachtsman to his safety harness, or is used as a lead or pulley for rope to run through. One side of the oval opens by means of

Fig 15   Classic abseil   *Fig 16   Half abseil*

a spring clip which on some karabiners can be locked, when it is called a screw gate. This type should be used for tying on in belays and abseils, as it cannot spring open which would be most dangerous. Another climbing technique for descending a very steep slope, or sheer face when there is no alternative, is abseiling. It is a simple principle of using friction to control the speed of descent down a rope. A turn of rope is taken round a belay point with both ends hanging down the slope. To abseil, stand astride the rope and attach it by one of several methods (two of which are described here) and move to the edge. Lean over the edge backwards until your centre of gravity is below the lip and then start to walk down. (It sounds so simple, but is scary when you have never done it before).

The Classic Abseil, as this is called, requires nothing other than a rope (preferably of manilla which does not stretch like nylon) passed round the body (as shown). The right arm is the controlling one (it does the braking) and the left the steadying one. The speed of descent is controlled by the position of the rope in the right arm; to brake bring it across the body, and to accelerate move it away. As the rope round the body creates the necessary friction, this method can be most uncomfortable and, if possible, padding should be used. At the very least gloves must be worn, wool or leather but never nylon, which melts under friction. On reaching the ground pull on one end of the rope to bring it down from round the belay. Except for very short descents of up to 9m (30ft), the Classic is best kept for emergencies when no other equipment is available.

The Half Abseil is used by mountain troops. A rope or tape

sling, either spliced or knotted, and a screwgate karabiner are required. Alternatively the Whillans harness can be used. The sling is twisted to form a figure-of-eight and then used as a sit harness; this is called an abseil strop. The karabiner is attached between the legs through both loops of the sling. The Whillans harness is reinforced by passing a small tape through the attachment loops and then clipping it into the crutch screwgate karabiner. The rope is passed around over the body and clipped into the karabiner (as shown). Descent is controlled in the same way as the Classic method. To lock off the abseil, the rope is passed in two figures-of-eight around the legs and tied off to the karabiner in a figure-of-eight knot.

The Arm Abseil is a simple method of descending easy terrain fast. A rope is passed across the back, over the top of the uphill arm, twisted around the lower arm and gripped in the hand. Descent is made sideways, controlling speed by the feet by twisting the lower arm and gripping with both hands.

Roping up and belaying can be practised on almost flat ground before graduating to slopes, but the novice should only try his hand at abseiling when protected by a safety rope in the hands of an experienced climber or, preferably, a qualified instructor. Without becoming a mountaineer it is still possible to find oneself in a position of having to do a little very simple climbing, or scrambling, to get round an obstacle or out of a predicament. The principles of movement on rock or steep terrain come under nine headings, which can be memorised by the mnemonic **CASHWORTH.**

1   **C**onserve energy: lifting the body through distances of vertical height necessarily uses a lot of energy. The best climber will do it in the least strenuous way by careful use of balance. He will always keep his centre of gravity over his feet so that arms and upper body do not take unnecessary strain, and most of the work is done in the natural way by his leg muscles.

2   **A**lways test holds: each foothold and handhold is tested as a routine before a climbing movement is made. This is done by

Opposite: Stepping off into space, a Royal Marine recruit starts on his first half abseil

Half abseil. A Royal Marine recruit using a rope sling knotted together and twisted into a figure-of-eight to form a sit harness. He steps into the figure-of-eight, pulls it between his legs, and joins the two loops of the eight together with a screwgate karabiner

tapping the rock with hand or foot and listening for a hollow sound, which indicates instability, or by feeling or seeing that a hold is loose.

3 Stand upright: novices often make the mistake of clinging too close to the rock face. This is a natural instinct, but a dangerous one, because the centre of gravity imparts an outward thrust to the feet which on a narrow ledge could easily slip off. Friction of clothing against the rock makes it harder to move, and clothing and equipment could become snagged. The face is also too near the rock, obstructing the view of footholds and handholds. The correct stance is upright, with the centre of gravity running through the body to the soles of the feet so that the weight of the body increases their grip. It is

95

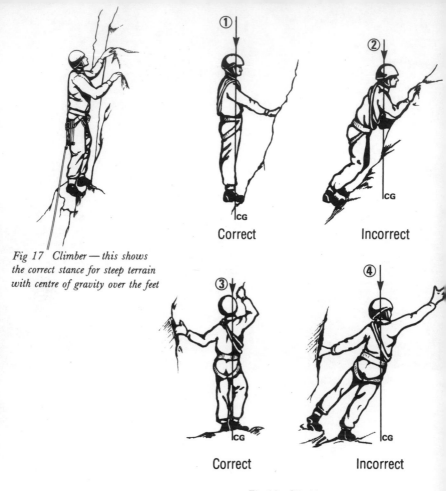

Fig 17   Climber — this shows the correct stance for steep terrain with centre of gravity over the feet

Correct   Incorrect

Correct   Incorrect

Fig 18   Climbing stances

also easier to move and look around in that position.

4   **H**ands low: where practical, keep the hands at shoulder level so that the blood supply to arms and hands is not reduced, and so as to avoid the extra strain on arm and shoulder muscles by having to make a high pull up.

5   **W**atch your feet: to maintain balance and to ensure that most of the work is being done by the leg muscles, a climber

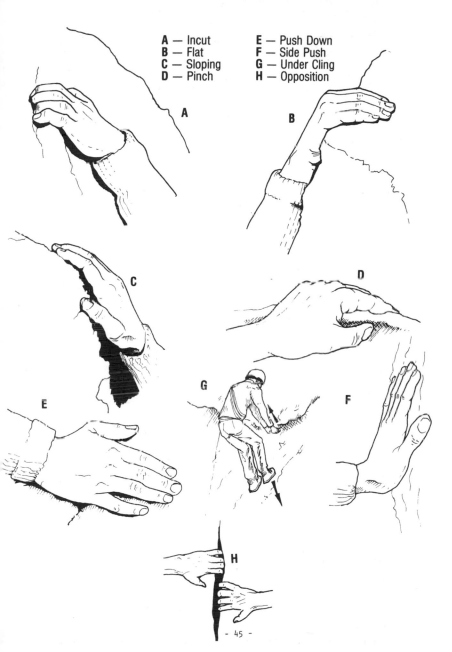

A — Incut
B — Flat
C — Sloping
D — Pinch
E — Push Down
F — Side Push
G — Under Cling
H — Opposition

Fig 19 Hand holds

97

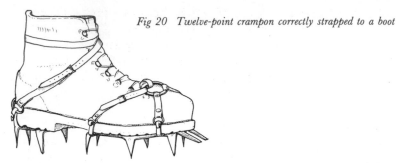

Fig 20   Twelve-point crampon correctly strapped to a boot

must watch where he places his feet. Any movement of feet must be cautious, but positive, so that the centre of gravity remains over them. Avoid scraping the feet or making high steps, which indicates an unbalanced position.

6   **O**n three points: it is necessary to keep three points of contact with the rock, in other words only move one of the four limbs at a time. Then the climber can move on small holds and always have two points of support should one hold give way.

7   **R**hythmic movement: the hallmark of a competent climber is a slow and easy rhythmic movement. Rushing, scrabbling, or muscling up on holds is exhausting and dangerous. Decide in advance which holds to use and how, and then move deliberately and smoothly keeping a reserve of strength so that control and confidence are maintained and minimum effort used.

8   **T**hink ahead: take time and plan moves ahead so that any difficulties are anticipated, and the best way of overcoming them is already worked out. This way unbalanced positions, strain and tension are avoided.

9   **H**eels down: the heels should be kept in a natural position, normally just below the toe level, unless an upward stretch is being made.

There is no need to go into the mountains to practise these principles; they can be done just a few feet off the ground on any suitable rock face or large boulder. So also can the basic handholds and footholds used by climbers, as shown in the following drawings, some of which should be fairly obvious.

There are two items of equipment used for snow and ice climbing that even the walker venturing above the snowline should carry and be able to use — crampons and ice axe. Crampons are a framework of spikes, attached to boots, for ice climbing and for walking on steep, hard snow-covered ground. The 12-point crampon is for climbing proper and allows ice and snow slopes to be scaled without having to cut steps. They can be fitted only to rigid boots, and that fitting must be done precisely. Buckled straps of non-freezing material are best, and they need to be tightened securely as loss of a crampon, once committed to an ice slope, could be disastrous. Instep crampons, which are more likely to be carried by the walker, are of little help for serious climbing, but will give considerable support on snow and ice slopes. They are also very useful for traversing rocks covered with verglas (a thin coating of ice or sleet). Although not intended for the purpose, they could be worn on slippery grass slopes where rubber-type soles cannot get a grip. For both situations, if you do not have instep crampons and have to negotiate slippery slopes, a pair of thick wool socks pulled over your boots will give you a better foothold.

There are three ways of using crampons — flat feet, front

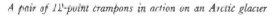

A pair of 12-point crampons in action on an Arctic glacier

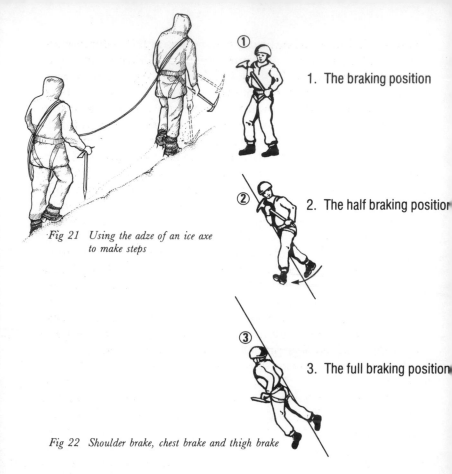

1. The braking position

2. The half braking position

3. The full braking position

Fig 21 Using the adze of an ice axe to make steps

Fig 22 Shoulder brake, chest brake and thigh brake

pointing and a combination of both. Using the flat feet method, the crampons are placed on the surface so that the maximum number of spikes are sticking into it. The climber flexes his ankles and knees, faces out from the slope and sits on his heels. When moving he crosses his feet, moving sideways like a crab. In practice, movements should be exaggerated to avoid crampon points snagging on clothing. Practice is required as it is an unnatural movement. Use front pointing to climb snow or ice; kick the toe of the boot sharply into the snow or ice to secure a firm hold. Weight is then transferred positively from one foot to the other, the sole of the boot being kept horizontal to the ground. In learning the skill on steep ice, short sections should be climbed without ice axes in order to develop a good balance. A combination of both methods has the advantage of relieving pressure on the calf muscles by using one technique for each foot and then alternating.

The ice axe head has an adze on the side and a pick on the other; the distal end of the shaft ends in a spike. It is a versatile tool that can act as a walking stick for much needed support on steep terrain as well as for cutting steps in ice, for self-arrest on snow slopes, as an anchor for a belay, for cutting snow and ice for shelters and, above all, as 'claws' to complement crampons when ice climbing. The adze is used with one blow in a pendulum movement to cut-slash 15cm (6in) steps in snow for diagonal ascents. The Pigeonhole Step is cut and scooped out by two or three blows of the adze, and its base steeply angled so that it provides a good hold for a mittened hand as well as a foothold. It is the step for climbing up steep snow. Step cutting in ice uses the same methods, but is very arduous and it is, therefore, necessary to have frequent reliefs to conserve energy. It is essential that steps are angled to give the foot a good purchase, and the Pigeonhold Step needs a pronounced lip if it is to be any use as a handhold.

If the hill walker or novice climber finds himself trying to cut steps in ice to get out of trouble he has strayed into the role of ice climber, which he is not, so until he has the skill he should stay away from ice slopes and glaciers. Acceleration in a fall down a snow slope is very fast because there is little friction between clothing and snow. The skill of self-arrest, using an ice axe, is something that anyone going on snow slopes would do well to practise. There are three positions to adopt:

1   The *shoulder brake* is effected by bringing the axe in to the shoulder with the shaft running parallel to the body while one hand grips the axe head and the other the lower end of the shaft. The pick is then gradually pushed into the snow by pressing the weight of the body onto it — if it is jabbed in it might be jerked from the hands. Keep the body slightly arched away from the snow face, with the legs apart for stability. If not wearing crampons the toes can be used to help break the slide, but if wearing them the feet must be held off the snow in case the spikes catch a projection and send the climber cartwheeling.

2   The *chest brake* is the more widely used method. The axe is held diagonally across the chest with one hand grasping the adze at the shoulder and the other hand gripping the bottom of the shaft at the hip. In very soft snow the pick is grasped and the broader face of the adze used as the brake. The full braking position is done in three moves: the above position is adopted before trying to brake or just before a fall; the body is then turned facing the side on which the axe is being held and the leg on that side is thrown over, but without the whole body rolling onto the shaft; the full braking position is reached by continuing the body turn until lying face down on the slope with the body arched and chest pressed against the shaft.

3   The *thigh brake* is for going down sitting 'side-saddle' on the snow when not wearing crampons. The pick is gripped by the uphill hand and the shaft by the downhill hand. The bent leg acts as a fulcrum for the axe, and the brake is applied by leaning gradually over the axe head. For practice, start with soft snow which will ensure a slow speed, allow easy braking and give a sense of security. Then go on to hard snow on a fairly steep concave slope free of scree, boulders and other hazards, with a clear run out at the bottom.

There are two techniques worth knowing used by climbers for getting out of a crevasse or for scaling a sheer rock face—the Prussik Knot and the Pulley System. The Prussik Knot is used for ascending a rope. It is made by taking a bight in a continuous loop of line twice around the rope to be climbed and then passing the bight through the loop (as shown). The knot will hold tightly when a weight is applied, but will slide freely when it is unweighted. Two of these knots are used — one attached by a short loop or sling to the harness at the climber's waist, and the other to a longer loop, forming a stirrup for one foot. The knots are alternately slid up the rope by the climber as he pulls himself up it; putting his weight on the foot in the stirrup, he pushes the knot attached to his harness as far up the rope as it will go. While that knot supports him he takes his

Opposite: Without any experience of climbing a recruit soon learns to move on a steep rock face using a rope

Fig 23 Self-help rescue

Fig 24 The pulley system

weight off the foot in the stirrup, which allows that knot to be shifted up. The knots work best when the supporting rope is taut; this can be achieved by suspending a weight, which can be hauled up afterwards, on its tail. Better than the Prussik Knot is the Ascendeur, a mechanical device that does the same job better.

In the Pulley System, the free end of the rope on which a man is suspended (or a second one) is dropped down to him with a loop tied on its end. He passes the rope through his harness or chest loop to prevent him falling backwards, then puts one foot in the loop. Holding onto the first rope, he brings his foot up as high as he can while the man above hauls in the slack on the pulley rope which he belays, then the man below stands up in the loop or stirrup. The process is repeated until he is hauled up over the edge. If the edge is soft, the shaft of an ice axe will provide a bearing to prevent the rope cutting into it.

If the edge is sharp ice, it will have to be trimmed so that it does not damage the ropes.

Avalanches are not just a phenomena of the Alps and other far away places; they are common, and always threatening, in our own mountains. No sooner is Christmas over most years than reports start appearing in the papers of climbers swept to their deaths in areas like Glencoe and the Lake District. There have even been avalanches on the South Downs. In Britain they may not have the magnitude of Continental ones, which sweep away hotels and bury villages but, for anybody caught in one, they are just as lethal. There are two main types — loose snow and slab — and they can be started by natural causes, by a skier or climber crossing a slope, or by a nearby explosion or vibration.

With loose snow, it begins near the surface as a small amount of non-cohesive snow slips down a slope and sets more in motion. A rise in temperature causes snow crystals to melt making the snow pack unstable. It only needs an overloading of new snow, or heavy footfalls, to start things off. These avalanches occur throughout the season, and can be wet or dry. A wet one is very heavy and dense, and when it stops it freezes into a solid mass of snow and ice in which no one could survive. Dry loose snow avalanches have enormous power; they can break limbs, sweep a person over a cliff or, falling onto a lower slope, overload it and start a second avalanche.

The slab form can vary between 100 and 10,000 sq m (120 and 12,000 sq yd) and normally occur on slopes of between 30° and 45°. The thickness of the slab can be more than 1m (3¼ ft), and on the way down will collect other masses of snow which will turn a small avalanche into an enormously powerful one. They are caused by sheer stress on the bed surface from heavy snow falls, or from redistribution of snow by wind, a shock load, vibration, a falling cornice, or a loading of one or more skiers. Another cause is too much tension on the crown, caused by the warming of the slab, contraction from protracted cooling, creeping of the snow or a sudden ski traverse. The run-out zone of an avalanche is a very dangerous area that can extend 300 to 500m (between 1,000 and 1,600ft) on a slope of 5° to 10° because the snow is much more dense in that area, having been smashed into small particles that freeze together.

Commando forces in the Arctic are very much at risk from avalanches and are given detailed instructions on their causes and behaviour. The safety and survival guide issued to personnel includes these basic rules on the subject:

Most avalanche accidents are triggered by their victims. Keep up *high* and avoid being the trigger that starts the slide

Keep clear of accumulation areas during and immediately after a snow storm

Lee slopes are particularly prone to soft slab avalanches

Never travel alone

Never expose more than one of the party to risk at any given time

Do not assume that the passage of another is proof that the slope is safe

Avoid cornices and the slopes below them

Fracture commonly takes place on the convex part of the slope

The most dangerous slope angles are between 30° and 45°

Avalanche slopes that run out into gulleys where the debris can pile up are especially dangerous

Thin forest offers poor protection, but below the tree line areas are generally safer

Take local expert advice and obey all avalanche warning notices

Know how to improvise a rope or ski stretcher

Find out the recent weather history

Be observant of warning signs such as booming of snow, heavy snow balling, fresh avalanche tracks, cracks in the snow when weighted, mini avalanches from the boots or skies

Sudden increase in temperature after a snow fall, especially with a dry wind, creates an avalanche danger

Study layers of snow by digging a small pit. Note particularly any weak layers and crusts

The deeper the snow the greater the danger. An accumulation rate in excess of 2.5cm (1in) per hour leads to avalanche danger. Snow takes 2 to 3 days to settle, and longer if the weather is cold and the area is out of the sun.

Action when crossing a potential avalanche slope:

Loosen ski bindings and take hands out of ski pole straps

Loosen rucksack straps and be prepared to shed any other impedimenta

Secure your combat jacket hood over your mouth and nose if possible

Go downhill on foot rather than ski

Go straight down rather than make a descending traverse

Cross high and if possible on a *concave* slope. It is generally more stable than other slopes, and the higher you are the less chance there is of being buried

Cross one at a time. Never assume that the passage of another party is proof that the slope is safe. They may well be the first pressure on the trigger.

Action if caught in an avalanche:

Remove rucksack and skis (these should already be in the quick release position if on suspect ground). A good skier may be able to ski out of danger

Make a quick assessment of the avalanche, whether you are at the top, bottom or middle or to one side and where your best line of escape lies

Delay your departure for as long as possible. The more you let past you at the start means the less will bury you at the finish. It may be advantageous to work out of the side of the avalanche

If swimming movements are possible, it seems a double action back stroke is the most effective with the back to the force of the avalanche and the head up. Obviously if there is a danger of being struck by blocks and slabs of snow then your arms will be used for protection of head and face. There is no clear cut procedure . . . ride out as best you can and save your greatest effort for the last seconds

Keep your mouth shut. In a powder avalanche cover the mouth and nose with some clothing and form an air space to breath in

A supreme effort should be made in the last few seconds as the avalanche loses momentum and settles. Two things are paramount — an air space and a position near to the surface. The chances of survival are greatly reduced if buried deep (4ft or more)

Establish orientation by spitting and then try to dig slowly to the surface

Above all . . . *do not panic.*

Avalanche search:

Speed is of paramount importance in any avalanche search operation. The chances of survival are greatly reduced as burial time increases. Few victims are brought out alive after two hours or more in the snow

Mark the position where the victims were engulfed and when last seen. The line between the two points will indicate the direction of flow

A search of the debris must be made for any sign of the victims or their equipment. *No longer* than half an hour should be spent on this search

A coarse probe search must then be instituted. If nothing is found then repeat the search

Finally a fine probe search should be carried out if the victim or victims have not been found.

Normally only specialist rescue teams would carry these probes so instead ordinary individuals would have to use reversed ski poles, the back ends of skis or tree branches. Parties who know they will be going into avalanche areas would do well to invest in small transmitter/receivers which are now available as small as cigarette packets.

CHAPTER 10

WATCH THE WEATHER

The weather in mountainous areas is notoriously fickle and can change very quickly from pleasant, warm sunshine to gloomy skies and driving rain or a blizzard. Mountains cause air currents to be uplifted and disturbed, so they attract prolonged periods of severe weather conditions. A mountaineer need not have a detailed knowledge of meteorology, but he must know where to obtain a reliable weather forecast before venturing into a mountainous environment in order to avoid unnecessary risk. The wind blows most strongly on mountain tops and across ridges because its speed increases with height. A strong wind can be very tiring, as considerable energy is used to balance while being buffeted. It also cools the body quickly by removing generated heat. A combination of low temperature and strong winds can be most dangerous, causing quick chilling. Rain is more frequent and heavier in such areas too. Once clothing is wet it will conduct heat away from the body because water is a good heat conductor, while trapped air pockets in dry clothes are not; in fact, when wet, insulation is cut to only 10 per cent. Reduced visibility caused by low cloud, driving rain, mist, whiteout conditions or storm will cause navigation problems. Wet rocks and grassy slopes are slippery and, thus, potentially dangerous.

An increase in altitude will cause a lowering of temperature, termed the lapse rate, and possibly a change in weather. Low temperatures cause body heat loss, and below freezing will also cause verglas to form on rock whenever water is present. Dehydration may occur in cold temperatures if too many garments are worn and overheating occurs; likewise the effort involved in negotiating steep terrain can produce the same result in hot weather.

Lightning is very dangerous to a mountaineer as it is

attracted to summits and pinnacles and then discharges down the mountainside. Many mountaineers have lost their lives due to it. Therefore, in a thunderstorm avoid summits, pinnacles, exposed ridges, gullies containing water and lone trees. Overhangs and recesses in cliffs give no protection against a discharging earth current, and metal equipment and wet ropes should, where possible, be left at least 15m (50ft) from the place of shelter. Vertical cliffs are good conductors, so should be avoided. A sitting position with the knees drawn up against the chest is the best protection against earth currents.

Every opportunity for getting updated weather forecasts should be taken. Radio and television give 24 hour general forecasts, and the shipping forecasts can be useful as they indicate weather approaching from offshore. The best source is the personal weather service, which can be obtained by telephone from local meteorological offices around Britain. It is important to give the exact area and time required for the forecast. The valley and mountain top weather, winds, temperatures, visibility, type of precipitation, freezing level and any changes should be asked for. All airports, civil and military, have instant access to the latest forecasts.

For weather forecasting an altimeter, which gives you your altitude, has a very useful second function as a barometer. The following rules for changes in pressure usually hold true and can be applied to give more meaning to changes in barometric pressures:

1   If there is an appreciable rise in pressure in the span of only a few hours, the fine weather indicated will be short-lived.

2   If pressure rises rapidly during a period of a day good weather can be expected, and its duration will depend on the amount of the rise. If a rise only lasts a day, the good weather will not last much longer either.

3   If pressure keeps rising slowly and uniformly for two or more days, a long spell of dry weather will follow. If, at the same time, the wind veers from west to north, the existing weather will quickly clear.

4   If the wind veers from south through west to north, with a pronounced rise in pressure, the weather will improve.

5   If the pressure goes up to an unusually high level with a moist atmosphere during a period of calm conditions, then fog

or mist can be expected, which will probably be followed by good weather.

6   If the pressure rises rapidly but erratically interspersed with small falls then expect unsettled weather. The same is indicated by rapid and spasmodic falls in pressure with some brief rises.

7   The wind veering from north, or east, to south or south west with falling pressure at the same time, means rain.

8   A long and continuous drop in pressure indicates a long and continuous period of rain, and the greater the fall the longer the rain will persist. If the pressure falls rapidly to a very low level, a downpour and strong wind are imminent.

9   In calm warm conditions, especially in summer, a rapid but not too big a fall together with increasing humidity means a thunderstorm is coming.

10   If the pressure rises only in the afternoon, the fine weather that follows will not last long.

11   A fall that continues through the morning means rain soon. With wind in the west, the rain will come within 24 hours, but a bit later if it is from the east.

12   If pressure falls only in the afternoon it is of small consequence, especially in summer.

No amount of general meteorological knowledge is as helpful as genuine local knowledge in areas such as mountains and lakes, which have their own exclusive and erratic weather patterns. Shepherds, farmers, gamekeepers, foresters, members of mountain rescue teams, and those who have to work outdoors, can be sources of such knowledge. But beware of the hotelier, publican and others in the tourist business who are likely to tell you what they think you want to hear! Above all, remember that if the weather is bad in the valley, it will be worse on the tops, and if worsening weather is forecast, play safe and keep off the hills.

CHAPTER 11

COLD WEATHER SENSE

There is often a tendency in very cold environments for people to become lazy about preparing and eating satisfactory morning and evening meals, a habit that can very soon have a detrimental effect on both their health and performance. When engaged in rigorous activities in the cold, balanced meals containing fats, protein and carbohydrates need to be eaten three times a day, with snacks in between. You need more calories in the cold to meet the body's greatly increased energy requirements. This extra energy is needed for heating the air you breathe in, for making up body heat lost to the cold and for the effort of moving about in snow wearing heavy clothing and a backpack. If you do not get the calories you need, your efficiency will fall off noticeably in a very short time and result in fatigue, listlessness and instability. Always eat your fill when you get the chance. (Cold climate food is discussed in the next chapter).

In cold regions, as elsewhere, the body will not operate efficiently without adequate water, although one does not feel as thirsty in cold as in hot weather. Fluids must be taken with all meals and in between, and hot drinks are preferable to cold since they warm the body as well. Alcohol must not be taken in the open as it is quickly absorbed into the bloodstream and produces vasodilation (expansion of the blood vessels), which draws warm blood from the core to the body's surface where its heat is lost, thus bringing about an overall cooling of the body. It must *never, never,* be given to exposure victims, but it is sometimes given under medical supervision in cases of frostbite if there is no risk of subsequent exposure. It is better to take water from streams or lakes (with the proviso that it be boiled) than by melting snow, which is a slow process and uses up large quantities of fuel. It takes 278 cu cm (or 17 cu in) of

Marine Commandos melting ice for a brew-up in their snow hole

unimpacted snow to produce only 16·4 cu cm (or 1 cu in) of water. Ice melts more quickly and provides the same volume of water. To keep open a natural supply of running water, cut a hole through the ice of a stream or lake and then cover it with snow blocks, boarding or anything stiff and flat onto which snow can be piled to provide insulation to stop the hole freezing over.

Cold weather is healthy weather, providing you look after your body and know how to behave when the temperature drops below zero. Then everything takes just that much more effort, but if you are fit you will not easily become exhausted. Cleanliness is not just next to Godliness, but an essential part of keeping healthy in the field. Wash hands and face daily and dry them completely. Feet, crutch and armpits should be washed at least twice a week, and more if possible. Stale perspiration and body oils combined with dirt are very conducive to skin infections which will not respond well to treatment in the cold. Moustaches are a great nuisance, unless they are kept short, because they grow icicles from moisture in the breath and may mask the presence of frostbite. Shave every day, but do it just before turning in for the night. Boots and socks should be removed every night, the feet washed, if possible, and massaged, and socks turned inside out to prevent

113

matting. Tooth and gum infections are more painful in the cold, so clean them well every day. A toothpick and a good rinse after a meal would be sensible — remember that extra intake of sugar and sweets would not please your dentist. If underwear, shirts and sweaters cannot be changed at least twice a week, they can be crumpled, rubbed together, shaken out and then aired for about two hours; compression reduces the fluffiness of wool and, therefore, the volume of insulating air that it can hold.

In freezing cold always try to breathe through your nose. The Commandos have found that it is the mouth-breathers who most often get dry, hacking coughs and chest problems in the Arctic. The air passages of the nose start warming the air before it gets into the lungs. Cold air is the cause of a lot of upper respiratory tract infections in the Arctic, and the medics say that the larger percentage of such infections are among smokers who fare badly, as do those who share a tent with them. Smokers should give up the habit before going into an Arctic environment, but if they leave it until they get there, it is better to stop smoking gradually rather than suddenly. There have been a number of cases of smokers getting chest infections through giving up cigarettes overnight on arriving in Norway, instead of doing the harder thing—smoking only 1 or 2 a day to keep their cough reflex going.

Dehydration occurs in severe cold when men cannot be bothered to discard clothing when they are overheated and are exerting themselves or are heavily laden, with the result that they perspire and start heavy breathing. Both ways they lose body moisture, which can be difficult to replace. Water bottles freeze, melting snow is tedious and time consuming, and a thermos does not hold much liquid for its bulk. One answer is to take everything a bit slower, find a pace and weight of clothing with which you can keep warm without sweating, and allow time for making drinks. Ventilation stops are important in order to avoid overheating. Stop when you start to perspire, reduce the amount of clothing or at least loosen the neck and cuffs of your anorak. Movement generates heat, but if you are stopping for more than a few minutes replace clothing and wrap up well as you need remain static for only a minute or two before you feel chilly.

CHAPTER 12

FOOD FOR ENERGY

Six essential requirements are needed in a diet for active persons: carbohydrates, protein, fats, water, minerals and vitamins. The first three are the basic foodstuffs for energy and the production of new tissue. Carbohydrates—bread, potatoes, pasta, cereals and fruit — are the quickest and most efficient source of energy. They are easily broken down into glucose and used for energy, or converted into glycogen which is stored in the liver and muscles and determines how long a person can function before becoming exhausted. Protein is used mainly for growth and repair of tissue and only as a secondary energy source. Obtained from meat, fish, dairy products, grains, peas, beans and nuts, proteins take 4 to 6 hours to digest, for which reason they are not ideal as an energy boost before strenuous exertion.

Fat is the form in which the body stores fuel and, although only a secondary source of energy, it makes up about 40 per cent of the average modern diet, which is far too high for healthy living. Excess fat deposits result in stress on the heart and joints and in an all-round decrease in the function of the body. However, when fat is burnt up by exertion it provides twice as much energy as carbohydrates, but it is more difficult to digest and metabolise so, again, it is not much use as a preparation for immediate hard work. Carbohydrates remain top of the list as the quick energy fuel. Water is essential to life, and in normal circumstances more than $2l$ (2qt) should be drunk daily to flush waste products from the body. Insufficient water intake leads to muscle cramps, and in hot weather to heat exhaustion.

Mineral salts — sodium, calcium, phosphorus and iron — which are essentials, come in sufficient supply with a well mixed diet of animal and vegetable foods. Salt and potassium,

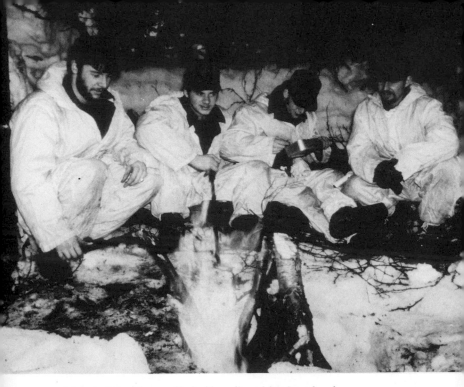

A lean-to bivi with snow block side walls and brushwood roof

which are required for muscular contraction and relaxation, are found in bananas, potatoes, oranges, meat, poultry and fish. Iron supplements may be needed for heavy training. A properly balanced diet will provide all the vitamins needed for an active person. It is a fallacy that vitamin supplements taken in quantity will improve performance, but there is a case for a person in heavy training taking extra vitamins B, C and E and for increasing protein intake while muscle is being built.

The energy value of food is expressed in calories, and the average man is presumed to need about 3,000 a day and a woman about 2,000, but strenuous activity pushes up the demand. The activities of Royal Marines out on exercises, or in an operational role, can be likened to the civilian taking part in very strenuous outdoor activity or adventure sport. So what the Marines are given to eat in these circumstances could well be used as a guide to the type and quantity of food that a civilian might consider carrying as his rations. The 24hr army ration pack has a nutritional value of 4,000 calories when issued for temperate climates and 4,500 calories for cold climates. The latter is designed to give a hot meal at night, with a substantial snack meal, which does not need cooking or heating, during the day. The pack contains a preponderance of dehydrated items (tins make for bulk and unwanted weight) and sufficient beverages for the high fluid intake needed in sub-zero conditions. The 24hr Arctic ration pack may not be gourmet eating, in fact the Marines do get pretty fed up with it after a few weeks, but it is well balanced and sustains them in the worst that the Arctic environment can throw at them. The civilian spending his own money could probably make up some more appetising menus while keeping to the same balance of content and quantity.

Royal Marines Commandos carry a more compact and less varied 24hr Arctic rations which would appeal even less to the gourmet, but they are adequate, and quick and easy to cook and eat — essential for troops who have to be highly mobile.

They have a choice of four menus:

Menu A	Menu B
BREAKFAST	**BREAKFAST**
Porridge	Porridge
Drinking Chocolate	Drinking Chocolate
SNACK	SNACK
Beef Spread	Chicken Spread
Biscuits, Fruit & Plain Chocolate	Biscuits, Fruit & Plain Chocolate
Chocolate Caramels	Chocolate Caramels
Nuts & Raisins	Nuts & Raisins
Dextrose Sweets	Dextrose Sweets
MAIN MEAL	MAIN MEAL
Chicken Soup	Vegetable Soup
Beef Granules	Curried Beef Granules
Mashed Potato Powder	Rice
Peas	Peas
Apple Flakes	Apple & Apricot Flakes

Menu C	Menu D
BREAKFAST	**BREAKFAST**
Porridge	Porridge
Drinking Chocolate	Drinking Chocolate
SNACK	SNACK
Chicken & Bacon Spread	Ham Spread
Biscuits, Fruit & Plain	Biscuits, Fruit & Plain
Chocolate	Chocolate
Chocolate Caramels	Chocolate Caramels
Nuts & Raisins	Nuts & Raisins
Dextrose Sweets	Dextrose Sweets
MAIN MEAL	MAIN MEAL
Oxtail Soup	Vegetable Soup
Mutton Granules	Chicken Supreme Granules
Mashed Potato Powder	Rice
Peas	Peas
Apple Flakes	Apple & Apricot Flakes

DRINKS: Coffee, Tea, Stock Drink, Sugar and Instant Skimmed Milk.

The cooking instructions for these rations could not be simpler, and nothing takes longer than 10 minutes.

Dehydrated Meat Granules—Add the contents of the sachet to a quarter pint of water and mix to a paste. Add further water if required and bring to the boil, then simmer up to 5 minutes stirring frequently to prevent sticking. (Allow Chicken Supreme to simmer for 10 minutes).

Rolled Oats for Porridge (containing milk already mixed)—Add mixture to a little cold water and make a paste, add a little more water and a pinch of salt, bring to the boil then simmer and stir for 4-5 minutes. Add sugar to taste.

Potato Mash Powder—Add a little boiling water to the powder stirring well until potatoes are the correct consistency.

Soup Powder—Add the mix to 1 pint of cold water and stir. Bring to the boil and simmer for 2 minutes.

Dried Peas—Cover with hot water, add salt, bring to the boil and simmer for 5 minutes.

Apple Flakes and Apple & Apricot Flakes—Pour boiling water over flakes in sachet and leave for 2 minutes to absorb the water. The flakes are then ready to eat.

118

Pre-cooked Rice — Place water in small mess tin up to bottom rivet and bring to the boil. Add rice and a pinch of salt and simmer for 5 minutes. Allow to stand for 2 minutes to absorb water. If you wish you can save a portion of rice to serve with the apple dessert. (The smaller section of a military mess tin filled to the centre of the lower rivet equals 1 pint).

Drinks — Individual sachets of tea, coffee and drinking chocolate make 1 pint each. The stock drink makes one-third of a pint.

The calorific value of the pack breaks down as follows: Breakfast: Rolled Oats — 300. Drinking Chocolate — 384. Both light and easily digested.

Snack: Plain Biscuits — 420. Fruit Biscuits — 500. Nuts & Raisins — 241. Paste — 140. Chocolate — 250. All high caloric mainly carbohydrate which is quickly assimilated.

Main Meal: Meat — 625. Potato — 140. Vegetables — 74. Soup — 214. Apple Flakes — 52. Sugar per packet — 112. Milk per packet — 48. Mostly fats/protein and long-lasting energy foods which should be eaten at night during rest to give the body a chance to absorb nutrition.

Water weighs heavy and there is a limit to the amount that can be carried, so rivers, streams, and lakes will more often that not provide the water for cooking and replenishing water bottles. But, before drinking, it must always be either boiled or purified with Puriclean, Aquatabs or one of the other proprietary tablets available from chemists and camping shops. A mountain stream tumbling into a crystal clear pool looks most inviting, but just out of sight upstream there may lie the rotting carcass of a sheep. In farming country too much agricultural chemical leaching into rivers and lakes makes such water unfit to drink. Whatever rations you take along, always keep emergency rations stowed untouched in your backpack. You could get caught by bad weather, somebody could be injured, and then you would need to feed them and yourself. Emergency rations can be very simple, such as chocolate, raisins, biscuits or any compact energy food to keep you going for 24 hours.

Your choice of cooking equipment and utensils must take into account both weight and utility. Bottled gas is heavy; it needs very good shelter from the wind, and is useless in the snow because the gas freezes. The classic British Army Hexamine stove folds flat for easy carrying, uses foolproof non-messy solid fuel and is cheap, but must not be used in a tent or enclosed bivi. The Trangia uses unpressurised meths, is lightweight and packs with frying pan and two cooking pots, but it takes 15 minutes to boil a litre (or quart) of water. The Peak One Stove is the Rolls-Royce of camping equipment; it boils a litre in 4 minutes using unleaded petrol. However, it is rather heavy at ·8kg (28oz) and costs more than £30. After considering weight and price, remember that the easier and quicker your equipment is to use, the more likely you are to be bothered to brew-up on a short stop and to take trouble to cook hot meals. The Optimus 2- and 4-man cookers which use Naptha de-leaded petrol are standard issue to the Royal Marines in Norway.

CHAPTER 13

HELP!

When an emergency situation arises — injury, being lost or weather bound — keep calm, don't panic, get into shelter, put on more warm clothes and think. Your mind will not work too well if you are cold, wet, tired and hungry. If you have time, if there is no immediate urgency, sit down and bring your mind to bear on the problem (light a cigarette if you must), keep cheerful, don't moan and hold no post mortems; it is not the time. Concentrate on assessing the situation and deciding on the best way to help yourselves. It may mean making a shelter, taking care of a sick or injured man, signalling for help, preparing some food or finding your way to safety. Stick together; unity is strength when things go wrong. Arguing without good cause will achieve nothing.

There is a limit to the amount of practical advice that can be offered on survival in a hostile environment in advance of the event. Frankly, if you do not get out fairly quickly, all the knowledge in the world about setting traps and finding the right toadstool to eat will be of little use. The most immediate danger is from exposure, and that applies to the fit as well as to the sick or injured. Being lost will not kill you — it takes a long time to starve or die of thirst, but you can freeze to death very quickly. So the first job is probably to build a shelter, but do not plan anything too ambitious likely to take a long time and use up precious energy.

Without doubt the best shelter is a snow hole, providing you have a digging instrument; no other material is needed, it cannot blow down and it is warm. Keeping warm is the important thing. You may have protected your extremities from windchill, but your body core temperature must not be allowed to drop. So get into extra clothes, into a sleeping bag as well, if necessary, or if you do not have one at least put your feet into your backpack. If your backpack has one, remove the lumbar pad and use it as a cushion to shield you from the cold underneath and thus prevent your own body heat being lost into the ground.

No warm clothes, no sleeping bag, no rucksack! It will be too late to remember the unbreakable rule that you never go off the beaten track anywhere without a survival pack suitable for the weather, the terrain, and the time and distance you will be travelling. A bottle of water, a chocolate bar, a waterproof and a spare sweater may be enough for an English summer's day walk, but on the mountains in winter a lot more needs to be carried — good energy-giving food, a small stove, extra warm clothing, waterproof top and trousers, a sleeping bag and bivi bag or tent. For what is definitely only going to be a day's expedition, there might seem little point in being lumbered with a sleeping bag, but in winter weather there should be at least a survival bag in a party for use in an emergency to keep an injured person warm until evacuated.

If you have a stove to produce heat, use it, but be careful to conserve fuel; its first use is to provide warm food and drink. If possible (and safe) make an open fire of brushwood, rather than of growing timber, which will be green, difficult to cut and difficult to burn. Food supplies both energy and warmth, so eat as soon as you can, but before doing so plan consumption to meet the situation. In a group, all food should be pooled and rationed out equally. The more you rest the less energy is used and the less food will be needed, so only exert yourself sufficiently for the job in hand. If planning to move on after sheltering and eating, rest a while first.

If others are aware of your plight, keep alert for anyone searching for you. Smoke by day and fire by night will pinpoint your position and so will flares. Coloured panels, or obvious patterns of clothes, will help searching aircraft, and in sunlight a mirror used as a heliograph will help catch the eye of an air crew, or search party on the ground, long before they see you. After all, when the weather was right the Romans sent messages from Hadrian's Wall to Rome in a few hours by using mirrors. Noise attracts attention; a whistle, or banging of cooking pots, will carry a long way, especially downhill, and if made in sequences of six at one minute intervals will, hopefully, be recognised as distress signals. Flares and smoke signals are excellent but expendable, so should be used sparingly. They are available as parachute flares, as handheld flares with a 60 seconds burn, as handsmoke (dense orange for 50 seconds) and as mini-flares in packs of eight with a one-hand operation projector pen.

The parachute flare, which rises to 300m(1,000ft), will be seen for many miles on a clear night and will take your signal up out of a valley into the sky above a ridge. On a bright day, in mist or against the sun it is almost invisible. It is no use hoping that one parachute flare will bring help unless you are operating in very controlled conditions with a base camp or rear party watching out for signals. A parachute flare burning for about 40 seconds may be seen by several people, but possibly only in their peripheral vision and in the last few seconds of the burn. They may not believe their eyes or may think they saw a shooting star, or may just ignore it. It might take two or three more flares, set off at regular intervals of a minute or longer, to convince the uninitiated that they have seen something worth reporting. But report to whom? How many of the general public would know to call 999 to get the rescue services alerted? Even if your flare is seen by a knowledgeable person, as it well might in a popular walking and climbing area, he is going to look for a second signal on which to take a bearing or at least estimate direction and distance.

Small handheld flares at night and handheld smoke in daylight are more use for pinpointing your position when help is on the way than for summoning it from a great distance. They are most effective when you have seen a rescue party approaching but they have not seen you. It is pointless setting off a flare to attract an aircraft that is flying away from you; save it until the 'plane or helicopter circles round again. From the air a handheld flare will show up in bright sunlight if it is against a dark ground, so try and be in the shade when you use it. Smoke is ideal for telling a helicopter which way the wind is blowing at your location. Mini-flares being very small — the size of a ballpoint pen — and contained in a waterproof pocket magazine are the most convenient pyrotechnic for the individual walker and climber. Although they do not make a big display, they are adequate for pinpointing your position.

It may be of some consolation to anyone in distress in heavy snow and unable to do anything to help themselves to know that the Commandos are taught that heavy breathing in extreme cold will produce local fog or vapour clouds that can be seen by the enemy. They are also taught that in cold still air sound carries much further than in temperate climates; the noise of coughing and skis breaking through snow crusts can be heard at extreme distances. If the temperature drops during the night, footprints will freeze and remain as direction marks. Above the tree line uncamouflaged (non-white) rucksack straps on a white-clad Commando at a distance of 1,000m (more than 3,000ft) will stand out clearly, and, because snow covered ground reflects four times as much light as bare terrain, any deficiencies in camouflage are exaggerated proportionately.

If there is no help available and you have to walk out but have neither map nor compass, then you could be in very serious trouble. At best prepare your mind for a long and worrying walk to safety. First try and work out where you would be on the map if you had one, and draw as good a sketch map of the area as you can on paper, or with a stick on the ground. The important thing is to put in a true north pointer. Then estimate where the nearest point of communication must lie, be it track or road, building or telephone kiosk. You have no option but to walk towards that point so, having made your choice, work out a bearing to it as accurately as you can. If you have made your sketch map on paper, mark on it the positions of the sun each hour during the day. With that sketch map, and using the hours on your watch, walk, keeping the sun in the correct relative position. Without a watch you will have to estimate the time, based on the fact that the sun rises in the east, is highest and in the south at noon and sinks in the west. During the night use the North Star which is easier because it does not move. But if you become lost at nightfall and are tired, it is better to find or build a shelter, then eat and sleep a little before making a move. At all costs pursue your plans relentlessly. You will have to trust your own reckoning because if you turn back you will become more lost than ever and more exhausted. Then fear and panic will take over.

When an emergency situation is due to accident or illness,

the immediate action is to get the casualty into shelter and made as comfortable and warm as possible while first aid is administered. How much aid can be given will depend on the competence of others in the party and what first aid equipment is carried. Strictly speaking, anybody leading a climbing party, or any type of expedition in a hostile environment or weather, ought to have sufficient knowledge to be able to treat shock, bleeding, broken limbs and exposure. A decision must then be made as to whether the casualty can be evacuated by the party themselves, or whether a rescue team and medical help will have to be summoned. If sufficient people are available then, after considering all the factors such as fatigue, experience and stamina, one or preferably two should be sent to get help, taking a written note of the grid reference of the casualty, location and all relevant details about the type of injury and the state of the rest of the party. The two messengers should take a note of their route and the terrain so that they can, if necessary, advise the rescue team of any problems.

When there is only one survivor, he must get his companion(s) into shelter even if only a windbreak, give what first aid he can and, before going for help, leave spare food, clothing, torch and whistle. If the companion is unconscious, leave a message where he will see it should he regain consciousness and put him in the picture. Unless the condition of the casualty were desperate, it would normally be unwise for a person to go off on his own during the night, unless he were very familiar with the area and absolutely certain that he could find his way to habitation or to a telephone.

CHAPTER 14

MAKING SHELTERS

During winter training in Scotland and in the Arctic, the Commando rifle companies stay out in the field for five days at a time, and for much longer spells during major exercises. Food, cooking equipment, clothing, bedding, a variety of tools, signalling equipment and other hardware (not least of which are arms and ammunition) have to be carried on their backs and there is, therefore, little weight margin left for tentage. Instead each man carries one tent sheet — a diamond-shaped groundsheet with button fastenings along its hems. To make a shelter, two or more men assemble a tent by joining together

In the Commandos each man carries a tent sheet which can be buttoned to one or more sheets to make tents for 2-8 men. Civilian parties could do the same thing using Basha or plastic sheeting adapted with Velcro or other fastenings

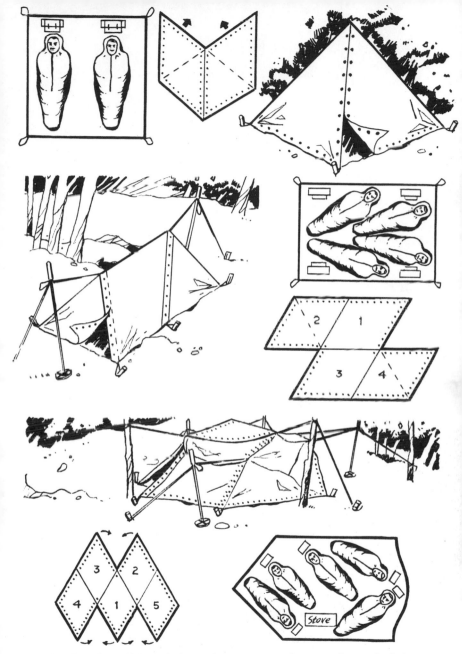

Fig 25 Tent sheet which can be buttoned to one or more sheets to make tents for 2-8 men

Building a lean-to bivi with snow blocks and brushwood on the roof

their individual sheets. They are issued with insulating roll mats and sleeping bags with waterproof outers to insulate them from the ground.

A similar, all-purpose waterproof sheet is a singularly useful item to carry as it can be used as a windbreak, rain shelter or groundsheet and, in kinder climates, could provide adequate shelter for the night. A civilian equivalent is the windproof and waterproof nylon Basha which measures 2·4m x 1·8m (8ft x 6ft) with 8 edge loops and one centre loop. It is usually supported by bungees attached to the loops. Where there is any overhead fixing it can be shaped as a rudimentary tent. Held top and bottom by stones as the third side of a triangle against a stone wall, it is an effective rain shelter. A Basha to a size of your own choice can be made out of the plastic sheeting builders use to cover cement, with a row of brass cringles crimped along each edge; a bit heavier than the 600g (21oz) ready-made nylon Basha, but much cheaper. If heavy duty Velcro were stuck along the edges of either type of sheet, two or more could be used by a party to make a tent in the way the Commandos use their tent sheets. Waterproof sheets and even small tents are, at best, a flimsy form of protection, and for survival in the Arctic Commandos construct more substantial shelters out of the natural materials of the area — trees, branches and brushwood in the tree line, and snow itself above it. Generally a snow shelter is warmer, and easier and quicker to make, than a brushwood bivouac, and on the barren wastes above the trees there is, of course, no option. On the other hand, in forest areas, snow usually lies rather thin on the ground and it is unlikely that any sizeable snowbanks will be found, so brushwood bivouacs have to be made.

Bivouac building is a very personal business depending on the individual's patience, imagination and the tools available. Certainly they cannot be constructed successfully without an axe, machete or large knife, preferably one with a saw blade, and — for snow shelters — some form of digging tool. A supply of string or twine is helpful. There are five classic bivi designs that are recommended: the single lean-to; the double lean-to; the wigwam; the tree pit bivi; the fallen tree bivi.

With knowledge of how these are made, it should be possible for a man to build a shelter under any conditions using a bit of enterprise. In a military context shelters should be built in a nondescript area of moderately thick woodland clear of roads and paths, and care taken not to disturb the natural appearance of the area by indiscriminate wood cutting and snow digging. Those precepts are, of course, made in the interests of tactical concealment. Similar rules apply in a civilian situation, but for environmental reasons, although in a life or death situation the easiest or the only available location is the right one. The instructions for building shelters, which follow, are based on those originally written for Commando troops learning survival techniques on their first deployment in the Arctic. As with all military training, a degree of perfection is expected.

The civilian in a survival situation who is cold, wet and hungry should not try to aim for anything near perfection. By the time he has built a perfect brushwood bivi or a classic snow hole he will have lost all his energy and will probably collapse before he can get into it. Initially he should just dig a snow trench, put a cover over it and get into it; or in the tree line erect a very simple lean-to. To keep a fire going requires an enormous amount of wood, enough hands to scavenge and cut it, and a watch system throughout the night to keep it going. Chopping wood will warm you, but when you stop you will soon cool off. Large and well made bivis are really only practical for organised expedition parties who will use them for longer than one night. The instructions for Commando forces are intended for survival in the snow, but when there is little or no snow bivouacs can be 'thatched' with turf and moss.

A *single lean-to* bivouac is built with its open side in the lee of the wind, otherwise it will be cold and smoky. The snow is cleared down to ground level and the main poles positioned (as shown on page 130). The top cross bar is placed at about shoulder height, and 60cm (2ft) of width is allowed for each inhabitant.

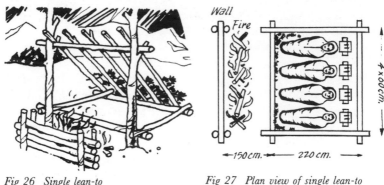

Fig 26   Single lean-to   Fig 27   Plan view of single lean-to

Fig 28   Heat reflection 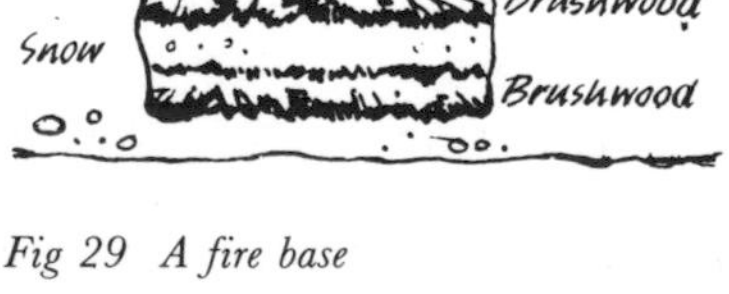   Fig 29   A fire base

A lean-to bivi with snow block side walls and brushwood roof

Fig 27 shows a lean-to that is just over 2m (6½ ft) deep to allow adequate space for a prostrate man with his rucksack beyond his head. Good strong timbers should be used for the main structure with a top cross bar 10 to 15cm (4 to 6in) in diameter. Once the main poles are positioned and firmly secured with string, intermediate and cross members can be put in. These are placed at regular intervals in the frame, but need not be particularly rigid. They are used to support the brushwood, which is cut and placed in a pile near the frame.

Shingling on the brushwood is done by working from the bottom of the frame upwards. The brushwood is woven into the frame with the stalk ends facing upwards, allowing plenty of overlap. The thicker the roofing the more sheltered and warm the bivouac will be. Snow can be banked round the base of the roof and walls to prevent draughts, but not near the top of the roof because the heat from the fire will almost certainly melt it and cause dripping. The floor of the bivouac is covered with brushwood to provide insulation. It takes rather a long time, but can be done by one man whilst the bivouac is being completed by his companion; ideally the brushwood should be 15cm (6in) thick. Once this is done, the rucksacks can be lifted inside and the bedding laid out. The lean-to bivi is completed with the building of a fire and a reflecting wall about 1·5m (5ft) from the front of the lean-to and extending its full length. The fire should also extend the full length so that every man has an opportunity to warm himself. It is important to build a good base for the fire if it is sitting on snow (see page 130). Finally, it is wise to cut sufficient wood to keep the fire in the whole night; stacked beside the bivouac it will help to keep out the wind until it is all used up.

The *double lean-to* for larger groups is built the same as two single lean-tos, but facing each other. The arrangement of the two structures is shown on page 131. This configuration is very economical on wood, as only one fire is built for two bivouacs and no reflector walls are needed. However, the layout is not very satisfactory in windy weather as the occupants of one or the other will almost certainly be troubled by smoke.

The *wigwam* is a very popular shelter because it is probably the warmest and most draught-free of all the brushwood bivouac types. Very big ones can be built that can house up to 10 men, but the 4-man variety is most usual and this is the size described and shown below. The first job is to clear the snow down to ground level. For a 4-man wigwam the diameter

Fig 30   Wigwam

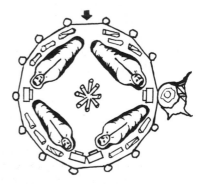

Fig 31   Plan view of wigwam

Building a brushwood wigwam bivi in the Arctic

of the cleared circle should be about 3m (10ft). If possible it should be situated under an overhanging tree or at least one whose trunk is a little out of the vertical. Such a tree will provide a very rigid support for the main uprights to be leant against. If no tree is available, the main uprights should be tied so that the structure is self-supporting. The poles for the main uprights need to be around 10cm (4in) in diameter and cut about 3·5m (11½ft) long. Once the main uprights are in, the intermediate and cross members are tied in place. These are placed at regular intervals in the frame and need not be particularly rigid. They are used to support the brushwood that is shingled into the frame from the bottom upwards in the same way as the lean-tos. The apex of the wigwam is left uncovered to allow smoke from the fire to escape. Once the roofwork is done, snow can be banked up round the base of the walls and, if it will stick, up to halfway up the wigwam. Having completed it, it is more convenient to build the fire base before putting in the brushwood floor. It should be designed as shown on page 130. Wood for the fire is best stored between the inner walls and the sleeping positions, then every man can easily stoke the fire as it burns down without getting out of his sleeping bag.

The *tree-pit bivi* can be quickly made for up to 4 men where there is reasonably deep snow in a wooded area by using the lower branches of a tree as a roof. Above this size such bivis tend to become rather unsatisfactory, as few fir trees have

Fig 32   Tree-pit bivvy

Fig 33   Plan view of the tree-pit bivvy

sufficiently widely spreading lower branches. The normal size is made for two men and this is the type described and shown (page 134). Select a large tree with thick lower branches and deep snow round it. The snow is shaken from the lower branches and the natural pit is enlarged around the tree trunk. For two men the diameter of the pit should be about 2·5m (8¼ft) and be dug down to ground level. If the snow is a little shallow, snow blocks can be placed round the top to raise the height of the walls; ideally, they should be at chest height. Entry steps can be dug out on one side and brushwood laid on the floor for insulation. Open wood fires are not satisfactory as the snow walls of the pit melt back and the shelter is soon destroyed. The best solution is to cook over a stove. If time is available, a tree-pit bivi can be improved by building a proper roof under the boughs of the tree. Poles are rested on the edge of the pit and tied at the other end to the tree trunk following the design of a very squat wigwam. Intermediate and cross members are then tied in and, finally, the whole frame shingled with brushwood, which makes the bivouac much warmer.

The *fallen tree bivi* is another quickly made shelter. It is made from a fallen tree or, if none is available, one will have to be chopped down. Ideally a tree with plenty of green branches is needed with the fracture height at chest level. If one has fallen and the butt end has broken off the stump, it can be lifted and secured back onto the upright bole, but it is important to

Fig 34 Fallen tree bivvy

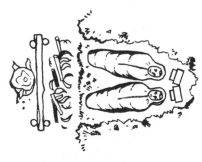

Fig 35 Plan view of the fallen tree bivvy

135

A recruit with his simple fallen tree bivi on a survival exercise on Dartmoor

ensure that this is done really well. The snow should be dug down to ground level underneath the fallen tree and the inside boughs trimmed off and used to thicken up the remaining ones on the sides. Figs 34 and 35 show a fallen tree shelter for two men. It is unlikely that a bigger one can be made satisfactorily. Once the side walls have been thickened up, snow can be piled up the sides to prevent draughts, and a good bed of brushwood can be laid on the floor. A fire base can be built in the front with a reflector wall beyond it, when the result should be a fairly cosy shelter.

Snow shelters come in three basic designs—the snow trench, the snow hole, and the snow house or igloo. The top of any entrance to a snow shelter should be lower than the sleeping bench to ensure that inhabitants will rest in a space of warm air trapped in the ceiling. The ceiling should be arched and smooth to prevent dripping. It will be found that ceilings will 'meltback' with age and the internal dimensions of a shelter increase. At least one snow shovel should be kept inside a shelter so that men can dig themselves out should it collapse. Some snow shelters are virtually airtight, so a ventilation hole must always be made in the roof; the 'ski stick hole' is the best type.

The *snow trench:* when operating on mountain plateaux or over barren wastes it may be difficult to find a snow bank in which to dig a snow hole. The construction of a snow house or igloo is one answer but, provided there is sufficient depth of snow, the easiest form of shelter is the snow trench. This, as its name suggests, is simply a trench dug in the snow and covered to provide better protection from the elements. Of all the types of snow shelter, this is the easiest and quickest to build. But while it offers good protection, it is not one of the most comfortable forms of shelter; it is cramped, and entry and exit can be rather a struggle. To build one at least 1m (more than 3ft) of snow is needed; the deeper it is, the easier the job. The first thing to do is to measure off and mark out an area about 250 x 60cm (8ft 4in x 2ft). Then, having put on waterproof clothing, dig out the trench. Snow spoil should be laid to one side for use in the roof later. If ground is hit before the trench is dug to a depth of shoulder height, snow walls can be built above snow level to gain extra height. If two men are to use the trench it may be possible to widen it towards the bottom so that the sleeping bench is 120cm (4ft) wide. The thing to avoid is making the top too wide because bridging it with a roof may present a problem later on. Once it is dug an entrance shaft can be scooped out. Before the roof is put on it is wise to get the rucksacks inside as it may be difficult to do this later. If possible, insulate the floor with brushwood, scrub or moss at this stage.

Putting on the roof can be done in a number of ways. Some form of snow cover is undoubtedly the best. Providing it is reasonably compact, snow blocks can be cut and laid across the top of the trench and then loose snow thrown on top to increase its thickness. This will provide a draught-free snug shelter. If it is not possible to roof it with snow blocks, there may be a chance of using branches and brushwood. Not many are required, and if the problem can be foreseen, a little wood can be cut before moving out of the tree line before lying up. A groundsheet can also be used to support snow if it is extremely loose. In extreme circumstances skis and ski sticks may be used as a roof support; this is not encouraged as it means that movement away from the area is restricted. The skis are placed upside down with the bindings positioned inside the trench to prevent them freezing. For emergency bivouacs when there are no sleeping bags, a snow trench can be made with the walls hollowed out to form seats on which the occupants can sit close together in their waterproofs with their feet in their rucksacks.

The *snow hole* is, without doubt, the best form of snow shelter. It is simple to build, comfortable and very warm. However, a decent sized snow bank or drift is needed. It is important to choose the snow bank carefully as it is not always easy to estimate the depth and height of drifted snow. It is well worth trying to establish the shape of the ground behind the snow bank; protruding saplings, wind-blown ridges and exposed moss surfaces or rock are often a useful guide. Having worked out the lie of the ground it is then relatively easy to judge the depth of snow on top of it. For a 2- or 4-man hole a drift 3m (10ft) wide and 2m (6½ft) deep is needed; bigger holes require proportionately bigger drifts.

The internal design varies according to circumstances. The width of the drift may determine the position of the sleeping benches. Personal preference will influence the siting of storage and cooking areas. However, it is generally accepted that there are only two sensible techniques for building snow holes. The first is called the 'tunnel' method and the second the 'block and cave' method. Of the two, the 'block and cave' is the quicker because all men can work at the same time, but this technique can only be used when the snow is sufficiently compacted to be cut into blocks. If it is not, then the 'tunnel' method must be used. Building in this way is perfectly satisfactory, but it takes longer and is a wetter business.

With the tunnel method the first job is to dig a tunnel directly into the snow bank. Initially one man only can work, but later on two are best employed. The front man can tunnel out whilst the second clears the excavated snow away from the entrance. Having dug in about 2m (6½ ft), it must be decided which way the sleeping benches are going to be. If there appears to be plenty of snow, it is probably best to have them on either side of the tunnel lying along its axis. If the snow bank is narrow, it may be necessary to have them at right angles to the tunnel. A snow block can be used to seal up the entrance, but care must be taken to ensure that a ventilation hole is kept open. The block and cave method is used if the snow is easy to cut into blocks. The principles for deciding the internal layout using this method are the same as when building by tunnelling. Having decided upon the total internal width required, men can dig straight into the snowdrift all along its width, so there is plenty of room for several men to work together. One man can set to work digging an entrance tunnel to the side of the main excavation. Once the snow hole is completely dug out, and sleeping benches and stove position established, the cave can be sealed up with snow blocks. These are best cut during the last stages of excavation as the snow is usually hard packed well into a drift. Furthermore, by using snow blocks from this area the minimum amount of snow moving is entailed.

The *igloo* or *snow house* is an excellent shelter in treeless areas where the snow is not too deep — after all the Eskimos have

Building a snow block wind break round a tent

used them for centuries. However, its construction of spiralling, specially shaped and interlocking snow blocks requires a particular type of snow and takes considerable time, effort and skill. Not least of the difficulties is finishing off the domed roof so that it will not collapse. It is therefore altogether too much of an expert job to warrant a full step-by-step description of the intricate technique needed. In any emergency survival situation it would be far more practical in shallow snow to build a cairn or pyramid of large snowballs to a height of about 1·8m (6ft) and with a diameter dependent on the number of people to be sheltered. Then dig away the snow to ground level on the lee side of the pile of snowballs and from there dig a tunnel into the pile, enlarging it inside to form a cave or hole.

Certain precautions need to be taken, while making and using a snow hole, to ensure safety and comfort. Digging snow is warm work, so strip off to avoid making clothes damp with perspiration, which may freeze later, and wear waterproofs while digging. Communications must be maintained with the man who is digging. Ensure that there is adequate ventilation in the snow cavity at all times. Always mark the entrance of a snow hole to ensure that you can find it again during the night; it also assists any rescuers should your snow hole collapse. Brush all loose snow from clothes before entering a shelter; this prevents them becoming damp in the warm atmosphere later. Put boots in a plastic bag before putting them in your sleeping bag overnight. Avoid having water simmering or boiling for long periods as this causes vapour inside a shelter, which will result in damp clothes, and have only one stove burning at a time. Sleep with your head towards the door. Always have a candle burning and keep a 'candle watch'; it will maintain a comfortable temperature and warn if there is insufficient oxygen. Building these shelters does require some experience of snow craft, and the techniques described should be practised before attempting any expedition into a snow wilderness.

CHAPTER 15

CASUALTY CARE

The survival of an ill or injured person when remote from qualified medical care will, in the first instance, depend on the competence of his companions and their knowledge of first aid. This chapter is no substitute for practical training and should be treated only as an introduction to the subject and an aide memoire in the field.

Every injury presents its own problems, but there are some general principles that are common to all cases, regardless of the treatment of specific injuries. Always remove a casualty from the cause or source of his injury if any threat still exists, but the most extreme care needs to be taken if he has to be moved before the full extent of his injury has been established. He may have suffered spinal or internal injuries, and any hasty or incorrect movement can kill or cripple. If he is conscious he will be anxious for reassurance, which must sound sincere. He will also hope that you know what you are doing, so display as much confidence as you can; a frightened man will be very sensitive to any sign of panic.

Injuries must be treated in the following order of importance or danger: 1 — Asphyxia; 2 — Haemorrhage; 3 — Shock; 4 — Fracture. Asphyxia and haemorrhage are the two greatest dangers, as either can cause death within minutes. Shock, which to some degree follows on all injuries, can also be fatal. Examination is best done with the casualty lying down and kept as still as possible. If he is conscious, he should be asked where he is hurt, where the pain is located. Except when haemorrhage is seen, or in the case of asphyxia, follow this logical sequence in your examination:

Check the mouth for broken dentures, blood and mucus that may obstruct the airway and, if necessary, clear the passage. Look at the head first, then the arms, shoulders, trunk and finally the legs. Clothing should be loosened but not removed in the cold except when there is a through-the-chest injury, when it will be necessary to seal any hole to re-establish a vacuum in the chest cavity and thus enable the casualty to breathe. If that action is overlooked he will die of asphyxia. If a bone is broken, or you suspect it is, do not move him until the affected limb has been immobilised. With vomiting or bleeding from the mouth, keep the mouth open and turn his head to one side to prevent blockage of the airway and to prevent him choking on his tongue should he be unconscious. Never try to get liquid into an unconscious person or into one with chest or abdominal injuries. In cold conditions he must be kept warm using either a casualty bag, a sleeping bag or extra clothing plus, when necessary, a waterproof covering. Never leave a casualty alone unless it is absolutely necessary to do so; company is in itself a form of nursing therapy. Once he is stretcher-borne ensure that the pace matches the ground over which he is being carried and the skill of the stretcher bearers so

Putting an injured man in a casualty bag prior to evacuation by sledge

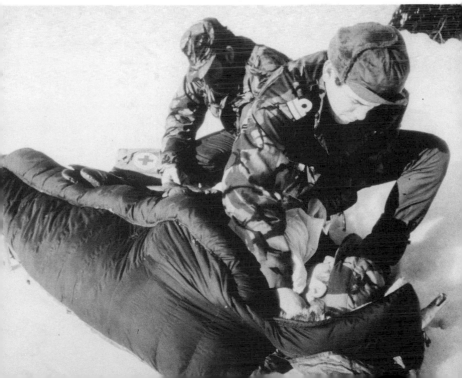

2. LIFT CHIN, PINCH NOSE.

3. BLOW INTO MOUTH, WATCH CHEST RISE.

WHEN BREATHING UNAIDED, TURN CASUALTY INTO COMA POSITION; STAY WITH HIM.

1. CLEAR THE MOUTH, TILT HEAD BACK.

4. WATCH CHEST FALL, THEN BLOW AGAIN.

GIVE HIM AIR!

5. AFTER 6 COMPRESSIONS — GIVE HIM AIR—ONCE! REPEAT PROCEDURE.

2. PLACE HEEL OF ONE HAND MIDWAY BETWEEN MID POINT & LOWER END OF BREASTBONE, PLACE SECOND HAND OVER FIRST.

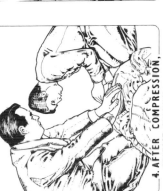

4. AFTER COMPRESSION, RELEASE QUICKLY, REPEAT ONCE PER SECOND.

1. LAY PATIENT ON BACK ON HARD SURFACE, FEEL FOR TOP & LOWER END OF BREASTBONE (STERNUM), NOTE MID POINT.

3. LEAN FORWARD WITH ARMS OUTSTRETCHED, SHOULDERS VERTICALLY OVER PATIENT. PRESS FIRMLY & QUICKLY.

DON'T LET HIM DIE! — GIVE HIM AIR!

Fig 37 Cardiac massage

that his 'ride' is as smooth as possible. A bumpy ride or jerky pace can be very painful and is liable to do more damage. Those are general rules. Now to specific injuries.

ASPHYXIA

Asphyxia or suffocation must be treated by immediate resuscitation. Lay the casualty on his back and clean his mouth and throat, if blocked, by using the index and middle fingers. If something is lodged in his throat, turn him on his side and slap him several times sharply between the shoulder blades before attempting resuscitation. Place yourself at one side of him, tilt his head back and pull up his chin so that the front of the neck is fully stretched. Make sure the tongue is not blocking the throat. Keeping the jaw upright with one hand, pinch the nostrils shut with the other. Cover his mouth with your own and blow air into his lungs every 4 to 5 seconds. Break your seal on his mouth between each blow. Continue in that manner until his chest begins to rise spontaneously and there is the sound of air leaving his mouth. When that happens allow him to breathe unaided. It may be a very long time before he breathes on his own, but you must persevere because as long as you keep blowing into his mouth there will be just enough oxygen left in your own spent breath to save him from brain damage or, eventually, death.

If after about 5 breaths properly administered there is no change in the casualty's colour, which should be turning from bluish to pink, it is possible that the heart is not beating and blood is not being carried to the brain, so neither is vital oxygen. Immediately check for a pulse at the side of the neck or at the wrist. If no pulse can be felt, or if the pupils are starting to dilate, then external cardiac massage must be started straight away. With the casualty on his back, feel for the top and bottom of the breast bone (sternum) and estimate the midpoint. Place the heel of one hand midway between the middle and bottom end of it and the other hand on top of it. Lean forward with the arms straight, shoulders vertically over him and press down firmly and quickly, depressing the sternum about 2·5cm. Then release the pressure quickly and repeat once per second. After 5 compressions give mouth-to-mouth air once and repeat the massage procedure when it is a

146

team effort, but if you are alone with the casualty it is advised that you give two inflations to 15 compressions.

It is better if two people are available so that one can do the mouth-to-mouth resuscitation and the other the external cardiac massage. The person at the casualty's head should be able to feel the pulse in the neck with each pressure on the sternum by the second person who can, from time to time, put his ear to the casualty's chest and listen for a heart beat. When the heart starts beating, stop the massage immediately, but continue ventilation until voluntary breathing starts. *Warning:* external cardiac massage has its dangers and is a procedure of last resort, to be used only when you are certain that the heart has stopped working.

In almost every case where a casualty is breathing, but unconscious, he should be put in the recovery or coma position by turning him onto his side (the damaged side if the chest is injured) and bending the top leg at the knee, leaving the bottom leg more or less straight. Gently pull the underneath arm out behind the body and the upper arm forwards in front of it. Bend the head and neck backwards so that the chin juts out and keeps the airway clear. Then tilt the head slightly down and to one side.

HAEMORRHAGE

There are three kinds of haemorrhage: capillary, when the blood escapes from a sub-surface blood vessel as with simple cuts and abrasions; venous, when it escapes from a wound in a steady and even flow and is dark in colour; arterial, when the blood comes from a damaged artery and spurts out in synchronisation with the heart beat. Then the blood is bright red in colour. Except in cases of a head injury, the casualty's head should be lower than the rest of his body to maintain a blood supply to the brain. Where a would is deep, blood loss can be stemmed by applying direct pressure to both sides of it with your fingers. Or put a dressing or pad on it and then apply pressure, keeping it up for about 15 minutes. If necessary, apply a second dressing should blood seep through, but do not remove the first one because the blood may already have started to clot — the body's own defence mechanism. If bleeding cannot be controlled by direct pressure, apply it indirectly to a pressure point between the heart and the wound. In an arm this is the brachial artery which runs along the inner side of the upper arm, and it should be pressed against the bone. In a leg it is the femoral artery which runs from groin to thigh; bending the casualty's knee, press into the centre of the groin with both thumbs on top of each other. Whatever you do, do not use a tourniquet except in final desperation. Left in place for half an hour it can lead to the loss of a limb. Pressure should never be applied to a scalp wound in case there is a fracture; it should just be bandaged.

SHOCK

Shock can be defined as a state of prostration resulting from a sudden fall in blood pressure. To a greater or lesser degree it follows on all types of injury, but is particularly associated with severe bleeding, external or internal; loss of plasma by burns or crush injuries; heart attacks; loss of body fluid (dehydration) from prolonged vomiting or diarrhoea; dilation of the blood vessels caused by pain and anxiety. Signs and symptoms to look for are shallow, rapid or irregular breathing; a weak pulse; cold, clammy skin; and violent shivering. The pupils of the eyes may dilate and be accompanied by extreme pallor. The casualty may feel faint or giddy and possibly have blurred vision. He may feel sick, vomit, complain of thirst, become anxious and suffer a lack of awareness or even lose consciousness.

Deal as best you can with the injury or cause of the shock while keeping the person warm and reassured. His legs should be raised slightly higher than his head and, if his injury does not prohibit it (eg damage to the digestive organs), give him a warm sweet drink. If there is injury to the head, chest or abdomen the shoulders should be raised slightly, with the head turned to one side. In the case of vomiting or unconsciousness, put him in the recovery position. Do not use any form of direct heating, as warmth can harm by dilating the skin's blood vessels. Covering sufficient to prevent him shivering and keeping him comfortable and insulated from the ground is all that is needed.

FRACTURES

There are five types of fracture: simple, when there is no

148

external wound; compound, where the broken ends of bone will show through the skin; complicated, when there is also injury to some important organ such as a rib penetrating a lung; comminuted, where the bone is shattered into small fragments; impacted, when the ends of bones are driven into each other. This latter can be difficult to diagnose as there may be no apparent discontinuity in the bone. The treatment is to give a strong analgesic and wait for it take effect before doing anything else. Then the priorities are immobilisation and evacuation. To immobilise, use a splint to reduce pain and prevent further damage. Never try to straighten an injured limb except a long bone (in the arm or leg) when, if you know what you are doing, you can apply traction by gently pulling the limb downwards before splinting it. Treat at the same time for shock.

PELVIC FRACTURES
Usually caused by a heavy fall of rock or debris or by being knocked down by a vehicle, pelvic fractures can also be inflicted by falling or jumping from a height and landing heavily on the feet with the legs held stiff. The casualty will have pain in the hip and loin regions, which is made much worse by movement, and will possibly have the thighs in an unnatural position. He may want to pass water but find it difficult, and his urine will be darkened with blood. However, the desire to pass water must be suppressed. Treat him for shock, give analgesics, then place him on his back with a pad under the crutch and the legs close together and splinted, or at lest tied together to help prevent the break from grating. When on a stretcher, do not secure any straps across the pelvic area.

LEG FRACTURES
The femur or thigh bone breaks rather easily in infants and in the aged, but otherwise it takes considerable force to break it. It is a serious injury because of the loss of blood into the surrounding tissue and the resulting heavy shock. Violent contraction of the great muscle mass of the thigh will cause the limb to point outwards. Give analgesics and, when they have taken effect, extend the leg slightly to stop the broken bone ends from further damaging each other, and then splint the

damaged leg to the other one. When available, apply a well padded splint to the inside of the leg extending from crutch to foot, and another on the outside from armpit to foot. Always keep binding bandages away from the fracture area. Doing this is bound to cause the casualty further pain. Treat for shock and evacuate to hospital.

Injuries to the lower leg can involve the tibia or fibula. Tibia fractures are usually open (compound) because this bone is only thinly covered. A fibula fracture, often the result of twisting an ankle, can be mistaken for a strained ankle. The damaged limb should be moved gently alongside the undamaged one, with padding placed between knees and ankles, then the legs bandaged together, but not over the fracture site.

BURNS

Burns are caused by dry heat—fire, sun, rope burns—and by wet heat — scalding or chemicals. Minor burns, with little obvious damage to the skin, can be cooled with cold water and bandaged. Severe or extensive burns, wet or dry, call for shock treatment, analgesics, cooling and protection with clean dry dressings and bandages. Burns caused by chemicals should be treated as severe, and all clothing should be removed from the affected area. The skin must be washed clean of the chemical with large quantities of water before applying a wet dressing which will not stick and will have a soothing effect. Never use grease, ointment or fluffy material like cottonwool on any type of burn. Burns can be exceedingly painful, which also contributes to shock.

HEAD INJURIES

Head injuries must always be taken very seriously; there may be damage to the brain. If there is, it may be obscuring the presence of other injuries to the spine, chest, abdomen or limbs. Because the skull allows for no expansion, even a small amount of blood from a haemorrhage can compress a part of the brain and cause damage. All head injuries require expert examination and prompt medical attention, so a casualty must be evacuated to hospital as quickly as possible. Symptoms, which show that the injury is more than a gentle knock, can be a slow pulse, shallow or noisy breathing, pupils of unequal size, unusual eye movements, grimacing or convulsive movements, varying levels of consciousness. A headache is to be expected, but it may be aggravated by bending forward or coughing. Very bad symptoms are paralysis and haemorrhaging from nose or ears.

Ensure that the casualty's air passages are clear, apply artificial respiration if necessary, and treat for shock. Where there is haemorrhaging on the outside of the skull, use a ring pad round the wound and then a bandage; do not put any pressure on the wound. If blood and other fluid is escaping from the patient's nose, wipe it gently and do not allow him to blow it. Do not try to stem bleeding from the ears; placing him in the recovery position will allow it to drain out.

SPINAL INJURIES

A fractured spine is a grave injury and, if the casualty is not handled correctly, the spinal cord may be permanently damaged resulting in paralysis. The symptoms include pain in the back, particularly below the level of the injury, and loss of sensation in the legs. There may also be loss of control over bladder and bowels. With neck injuries breathing may become difficult with the possibility of asphyxia. Spinal fractures can be suspected after a heavy weight has dropped on a person, or when he has fallen from a height onto back, feet, buttocks or head, or after jerking or jarring of the spine on severe impact. The victim may feel he has been cut in half, or has lost his lower half, which he can no longer feel. He should try and move his fingers, wrists, ankles and toes to ascertain if there is any paralysis. Even if there is no apparent loss of sensation, he must be handled with the greatest care to prevent possible damage to the spinal cord.

If a doctor is near to hand leave the casualty exactly where he is, tell him not to move and cover him to keep warm. In the field, away from medical aid, the casualty's shoulders and pelvis must be held still while padding is arranged between the thighs, knees, ankles and feet, then knees and ankles are tied together. He must be kept in a position that helps extension of the spinal column; padding under the back well above and below the site of the injury will help. Any bending forward is

151

extremely dangerous. Treat for shock and give analgesics, unless respiration is affected or other injuries preclude their use. Mouth-to-mouth resuscitation, if needed, has to be a calculated risk, as tilting the head back may cause more damage. The stretcher used to evacuate the victim will need to be stiffened with any material available to ensure the spinal column remains extended; in other words make sure the body does not sag. Lifting onto a stretcher without doing any further damage ideally requires four or more pairs of hands, as the casualty must be kept absolutely rigid. A blanket lift onto the stretcher is the safest method if that is available and there are enough hands.

CHEST INJURIES

These are most often caused by a direct blow, such as from a falling rock, or by someone falling onto a hard projection or, literally, flat on his chest. In cases of minor injury one or more ribs may be bruised or cracked and the victim will find it hurts to breathe and acutely painful to cough, but he can be given analgesics and treated as 'walking wounded', despite his great discomfort. It will make life easier for him if the arm on the injured side is held in a sling.

A major injury, or a complicated fracture, is a much more serious matter, especially if the injury has caused a wound in the chest thereby destroying the vacuum in the chest cavity (this will produce a sucking sound). It must be made airtight immediately or the victim will soon be asphyxiated. A pad can be held over the wound with tight bandages, but the best remedy is broad elastic adhesive bandage generously overlapping. In such cases do not administer analgesics, which will depress the breathing. While waiting for a stretcher, the casualty should be laid down with head and shoulders raised and body leaning slightly towards the injured side. Frothy blood dribbling from the mouth means that a lung has been punctured by a rib and makes hospitalisation even more urgent.

INTERNAL ABDOMINAL INJURIES

A typical reaction to an abdominal injury is that the victim pulls his knees tightly up to his chest. His muscles may be tensed, the abdomen be hard to the touch and he may vomit blood. Treat as for shock, but do not give analgesics unless evacuation to hospital will be long delayed as they interfere with subsequent diagnosis. If there is an actual wound, position the casualty so that it does not gape and apply a dressing and bandage firmly. Should an internal organ be protruding, cover gently with a gauze dressing or clean towel and secure tightly, but make no attempt to replace it. The abdomen should be supported if the casualty is coughing or vomiting. In all cases evacuate urgently to hospital.

Heat exhaustion

Work in very hot and humid climates, and excessive perspiring through exertion in hot weather, can bring on heat exhaustion. It can even be induced in very cold weather by overexertion while wearing too much clothing with no ventilation. It is not to be confused with physical tiredness or fatigue, although that may be present at the same time. Heat exhaustion is a shocked condition due to a deficiency of salt and water in the body. This latter can be aggravated by diarrhoea or vomiting. The signs are actual exhaustion, a cold pale face with clammy sweat and muscular cramps, a state that can deteriorate to collapse and loss of consciousness. It can best be avoided by wearing light clothing, which allows plenty of air movement, to provide heat loss through convection and evaporation of perspiration. At the same time fluid and salt loss must be replaced.

When Marine recruits have to do their 30-miler in the heat of summer they get doused with jerrycans of water at check points along the way. They set off with 3 pints in their water bottles which are refilled 5 times at the check points, and while there they are encouraged to drink as much extra water as they can keep down. On a hot day a man will get through about 11l (20 pints) of water, 90 per cent of which he will lose in sweat. A heat exhaustion sufferer should be cooled down and given plenty of liquid. Salt is no longer used in heat casualties as it can do more harm than good if not administered properly. The most severe form of heat exhaustion is hyperpyrexia, or heat stroke, which is a medical emergency. The first action is to do anything to reduce his temperature to below 39°C (102·7°F) as rapidly as possible — strip naked, sponge with cold water, fan.

Then give him a cold drink and salt. If possible, send for a doctor to give intravenous saline on the spot. If not, when temperature has dropped, evacuate to hospital.

COLD WEATHER INJURIES

Hypothermia (Exposure) is the great killer that stalks not only the frozen spaces of the Arctic, but also the exposed areas of our temperate latitudes. You do not have to be lost on a polar expedition to die of cold; it can happen on the rolling hills of England. Every year dozens of people, all reasonably healthy and uninjured, many of them young and full of life, die on our hills and mountains because they are caught out in wet, windy conditions when they are tired and inadequately clothed. We read brief post mortem reports in the press in which exposure is given as the cause of death, a term that may well describe the situation in which a person died but not the pathological cause, which was hypothermia — a drastic lowering of the body temperature.

Our bodies are a core that includes the contents of the skull, chest and abdomen, and a shell made up of the limbs and extremities, skin and underlying fat and muscle. The body maintains its core temperature accurately at an average of 37°C (98·6°F), while that of the shell is more variable but is generally about 3°C (6°F) lower. When the core temperature rises, more blood is circulated to the skin where it is cooled. This cooling can be increased further by sweating that is followed by evaporation from the surface. When the core temperature falls blood circulation to the skin is reduced, there is less cooling of the blood at the surface and the skin looks white and is cold to the touch. If the core temperature cannot be maintained with the minimum blood circulation to the skin, then shivering occurs. This is an automatic rippling action of muscle fibres which can produce as much heat (and as much exhaustion) as fairly hard manual work. Shivering is a visible indication that the body is cooling. The preservation of the core temperature is vital, as a fall in this leads directly to mental deterioration, the loss of muscle co-ordination and eventually to unconsciousness and death. Cold, wet and wind, especially when combined with wet clothing, are the main causes of hypothermia. Water reduces the insulation value of clothes to

Using the casualty's own skis and ski sticks to make a rescue sledge

one-tenth of normal; to make matters worse, when water evaporates it takes away whatever heat is left. The effect of such weather will be aggravated by exhaustion, which is often due to lack of fitness, to over-ambitious planning, too heavy loads and to too fast a pace. Lack of sleep and food before and during an expedition are common contributory factors. An exhausted body cannot tolerate even relatively mild cooling of the ambient temperature, being incapable of making the physiological adjustments needed to maintain body temperature. Some drugs, particularly those taken for psychiatric conditions, predispose a person to hypothermia — a factor which sadly is more pertinent today than it once was.

The ways of avoiding exposure and preventing hypothermia are all very much a matter of commonsense. Ample warm, windproof and waterproof clothing, including headgear and gloves, should be carried and put on in good time. Waterproof outer clothing is particularly necessary if there is any intention

155

of continuing an expedition despite the weather. Plan for a sensible (maintainable) pace, reasonable loads and the easiest routes to reduce fatigue and possible dangers. Good sleeping arrangements and ample energy-giving food both before and during an expedition are important considerations. Sensible leadership and the commonsense, even courage, to retreat from a situation are prime factors in avoiding the risk of exhaustion and exposure. Listening to weather forecasts, observing local weather, cloud and wind changes, studying the conditions of the hills, considering the time of year and the length of day, all help to make the onset of exposure conditions predictable.

To know when to stop and seek shelter and to treat an exposure victim calls for alertness on the part of everybody. The victim may start complaining of nothing worse than feeling cold, shivering and discomfort — which is how others may be feeling too — but there will be abnormalities in his behaviour that should be noted. They may not all appear or do so in any particular order, and some of them, being quite undramatic, could pass unnoticed. The first signs are likely to be quietness, apathy, a pale face, dropping to the rear of the party. He will be slow thinking, or fail to answer questions or undertake simple tasks he normally would do. He will start forgetting or ignoring such things as his gloves, his rucksack straps, and become careless with his footwork on broken ground. His condition will become very obvious to all if he starts doing unreasonable things, physically resisting help, shivering violently or having sudden bursts of energy. As hypothermia sets in the body tries to tell him by these bursts of energy that it is cold and needs to warm up. But each successive peak of energy gets smaller and each successive trough gets deeper. And in the end he will fall asleep, sink into a coma and die.

Early recognition of the onset of exposure will enable preventive action to be taken. Loads should be lightened and the route changed to go downhill or downwind, preferably both, and shelter found in the lee of a ridge or stone wall where a bivouac can be made with polythene bags, sleeping bags or whatever is to hand. A group can be warmed by huddling together with the casualty in a sleeping bag in their midst. If necessary, one person should get into the sleeping bag with him. Once in shelter, refuel with warm drinks and some energy food. If one person is suffering from exposure, then everyone in a group is at risk and must be checked for symptoms. Do not use a hot water bottle, rub the victim's skin or give him alcohol, any of which will cause a surge of blood from the core to the surface. The blood returning to the heart after being cooled on the surface will worsen the condition.

If caught in time, the casualty may recover sufficiently after warming to walk out unladen and well dressed following a sheltered route. More likely he will need to be evacuated on a stretcher so a full rescue operation will have to be initiated. Keep a semi-conscious or unconscious person in a slightly head down position and take care to keep insulation around him all the time. His face and mouth should be protected to minimise heat loss. Anyone suffering from hypothermia will be highly susceptible to frostbite too. A casualty who reaches base with his body temperature over 31°C (88°F) will almost certainly survive whether actively rewarmed or not. Active rewarming in a bath at 45°C (113°F) for 20 minutes can be done quite safely in such cases; he may faint when he is taken out of it. Rewarming a body when the temperature has fallen lower than 30°C (86°F) is a complex medical problem and should be done in hospital. If that is not possible the safest action is to allow the casualty to rewarm slowly in a warm room or heated shelter. Properly trained and equipped rescue teams, if they can be called, now have the facility to rewarm a patient in the field; they use a chemically-activated inhaler to get warm air into the lungs.

In cold and wet conditions on exposed ground, especially if there are also strong winds, leaders must keep a very careful watch on a party for the first signs of cold and exhaustion. At the same time, all the individuals in a party must also watch each other. It is vital that everyone remembers that one of the earliest effects of hypothermia is a dulling of the ability to reason clearly and, because of this, by the time hypothermia has started to take effect, it is already too late for that person to help himself. People have died of hypothermia with their salvation literally to hand in the form of extra food, clothing and even sleeping bags and tents in their rucksacks.

WINDCHILL FACTOR	The Risk of Frostbite on Bare Skin													
Wind Strength			Air Temperature C											
Beaufort Scale	Wind	MPH	+10	+5	-1	-7	-12	-18	-23	-29	-34	-40	-46	-51
0	Calm	0	10	5	-1	-7	-12	-18	-23	-29	-34	-40	-46	-51
2	Light Breeze	4.2	9	3	-3	-9	-15	-21	-26	-32	-38	-44	-50	-56
3	Gentle "	8.8	5	-2	-9	-16	-23	-30	-36	-43	-50	-57	-64	-71
4	Moderate "	13	2	-6	-14	-21	-29	-36	-43	-50	-58	-65	-73	-80
4	" "	17.3	0	-8	-16	-24	-32	-40	-47	-55	-63	-71	-79	-87
5	Fresh "	22.3	-1	-9	-18	-26	-34	-42	-51	-59	-67	-76	-84	-92
6	Strong "	26	-2	-11	-19	-28	-36	-44	-53	-61	-70	-79	-87	-96
6	" "	30.3	-3	-12	-20	-29	-37	-45	-54	-63	-72	-81	-90	-98
7	Moderate gale	34.7	-3	-12	-21	-30	-38	-46	-55	-64	-73	-82	-91	-100
			Low Risk of Frostbite				High risk of Frostbite			Very High Risk of Frostbite				

Fig 38   Windchill chart

SEVERE COLD EXPOSURE

Under certain conditions, for example falling into icy water, or after prolonged exposure to low temperatures, a person may appear to be in a state of suspended animation. The pulse and breathing will be slow, and he may feel cold and stiff to the touch. If breathing or heartbeat are absent, then mouth-to-mouth resuscitation and external cardiac massage should be started. In either case, while waiting for urgent evacuation, the very best treatment then is to put the casualty between two warm bodies with a dry covering over them; all three in two zipped-together sleeping bags would be ideal.

FROSTBITE

Frostbite is a condition found in dry cold below 0°C (32°F). It occurs when a part of the body is chilled and the blood supply to that part diminishes. If the chilling is brief the blood flow is only temporarily interrupted and no damage occurs, but if the chilling is intense and continuous there is a complete constriction and no blood to the part. The degree of damage then depends on the length of time over which this happens. There are three different stages — frostnip, superficial frostbite and deep frostbite. It is easier to prevent frostbite or to stop it in its early stages than to thaw and take care of badly frozen flesh. The only form of frostbite that should be treated on the spot is frostnip.

Frostnip occurs on exposed skin, such as the face and hands, and there is numbness accompanied by blanching, and a sudden and complete cessation of cold or discomfort in the injured part, which may be followed later by a feeling of warmth. Any sign of frostnip must be thawed immediately by warming the affected part, which is best done sheltered from the wind. Fingers should be warmed in the armpit or groin, and feet on the abdomen of another man! Once the part has been restored to normal colour, a person may continue with what he was doing.

In *superficial frostbite* the skin, though white and frozen on the surface, is soft and pliable when pressed gently. After warming, the part becomes numb, mottled blue and purple, and will sting or burn and swell for a period. Blisters may occur within 24 to 36 hours and will slowly dry up; the skin will harden and become black, producing thick, insensitive tissue. Some swelling may occur which will subside if the injured part can be raised above the level of the body. Throbbing or aching may persist for several weeks. When the black skin finally separates, the exposed tissue will be red, tender and usually sensitive to cold and heat and may show evidence of abnormal sweating. Only after some months will it take on the appearance of normal skin.

Deep frostbite involves not only the skin and underlying tissue, but also the deeper structures including muscle, bone and tendon. The symptoms are a more severe form of those of superficial frostbite. The skin becomes yellowish and lacks mobility. It has a waxy feel and does not regain its shape after pressure. Large blisters form after three to seven days and the skin turns mottled blue or grey. Shooting or throbbing pain can last for up to two months. There will be swelling, blisters and colour changes where the affected part joins unaffected flesh, and then the affected part slowly turns black and shrivels in size. The blisters eventually dry up, blacken and slough off, sometimes in the form of a complete cast of a finger or toe. The red, sensitive layer of new skin sweats excessively and itches for many months. As tendons are markedly resistant to cold injury, the victim will be able to move fingers or toes, and even with severe frostbite can often walk and use his fingers for crude movements such as gripping. Casualties should be treated by rapid rewarming, the affected part being placed in warm water at a constant temperature of about 44°C (111°F) until sensation returns. (A temperature of 44°C is that which an elbow immersed in the water can just bear.) This is an agonising procedure and pain-killing drugs are usually needed. This can only be done after evacuation and under medical supervision. Otherwise a loose sterile dressing and bandage should be applied, and the casualty given warm, sweet drinks and treated for shock whilst awaiting evacuation. The affected part must never be massaged or rubbed (either alone or with snow, oil or grease). A frozen foot should not be thawed if walking is essential as less damage is done by walking on a frozen foot than on one that has been thawed.

SNOW BLINDNESS

The eyes are extremely sensitive to ultra-violet rays which are reflected off snow, and snow blindness is likely after a fresh fall or during a prolonged white-out unless precautions are taken. The risk is increased at high altitudes. Such casualties are often victims of their own carelessness in not carrying goggles or in not putting them on until eye discomfort is felt. A deep burn may already have occurred by the time pain is felt. The symptoms are irritation and a gritty feeling, hot sticky eyes and watering. Vision may be blurred, and there is likely to be pain in and over the eyes and a headache. The only effective remedy is rest in darkness with a blindfold. If alone, a person should get into a dark shelter while partial vision remains. Quite minor cases can take up to 18 hours to fully recover.

DEHYDRATION

The incidence and dangers of dehydration can extend from temporary incapacity to, in extreme cases, death; the degree of incapacity depends to a large extent on the ability to recognise the symptoms at an early stage. They are: a general feeling of tiredness and weakness; the mouth, tongue and throat become parched and swallowing is difficult; general nausea accompanied by spells of faintness, dizziness and vomiting; muscular cramp especially in the legs; the urine turns a dark orange. It is best dealt with by prevention, which means a regular and adequate intake of fluids and salt. With an intake of between 2 and 5l (3½ and 8½ pints) of fluid a day and with sensible rations, dehydration will not happen. A casualty should be kept warm, but the clothing should be loosened to allow good circulation and the patient given liquids and salt gradually; one level teaspoon (5g) of salt in 2l (3½ pints) of water is palatable. Allow him plenty of rest.

TRENCH FOOT

When feet are exposed to non-freezing cold and wet conditions they can suffer from a condition called *immersion foot* or *trench foot,* so endemic in World War I and also a cause of casualties in the Falklands War because of the cold, wet conditions. The blood cells at the surface are damaged and the foot becomes swollen and painful. This is most likely to happen after long periods of sitting or standing without exercise in cramped conditions, and can be exacerbated by tightly fitting footwear. Pain and numbness may alternate and, if the pain is severe, the casualty will look ill and shocked. Eventually, if not treated, legs will also swell badly, and the skin will become livid or purple and blister. The all-too-obvious treatment of rubbing and warming is wrong. The foot must be handled very gently so that neither blisters nor skin is broken. Cleanse the foot, elevate it to help reduce the swelling, and keep it cool but covered from the cold by a blanket over an improvised cage to avoid contact. Hot drinks and food with aspirin will help. Evacuate to medical care as soon as possible.

THE BUDDY SYSTEM

The Royal Marines are committed to a Commando role that, by definition, means being able to operate in small groups, in hostile environments with the minimum of logistic support, if any, and possibly having ultimately to live off the land. To survive, let alone achieve any success, within those parameters every man however junior or senior must be highly self-reliant and at the same time caring of his comrades who will be his strength, and he theirs. A manifestation of that need is the 'buddy system' which was developed in the Arctic where men were paired to watch each other for signs of exposure and frostbite. It means that no man walks alone; he always has a buddy who watches, protects, helps and encourages him and he, likewise, is his buddy's keeper. It has been extremely effective in preventing cold injuries ever becoming a problem during the Marines' annual deployments in the Arctic, and was a great sustaining factor during the overloaded forced marches of the Falklands battle.

The buddy system is to be recommended to all who would venture against the elements.

CHAPTER 16.

LIVING OFF THE LAND

During their time at the Commando Training Centre young recruits spend three days and nights out in the open on Dartmoor as part of their survival training. Apart from the clothes they are wearing — fatigues — they may take nothing, not even a snack, with them, only a pocket survival kit contained in a tobacco tin. They have three very active days with two crosscountry marches and a night march, as well as having to build bivouacs and set traps and snares. They very rarely catch anything — the wild creatures of Dartmoor can surely smell a crowd of recruits a mile off — and the only sustenance they get is on the third day when they are each given a rabbit to slaughter, skin, butcher, cook and eat without any utensils.

The object of the exercise is, presumably, to give them an idea of what it would be like to be living off the land in a covert operation or as escaped prisoners-of-war in enemy country. What it does prove is that, being fit, they can go cold, wet and hungry for three days and nights and still function efficiently. And so, too, should any fit civilian who could find or make a shelter, especially if he had the survival sense to be carrying some emergency food. There has been much written about living off the land — laying traps, hunting with makeshift bow and arrow or catapult, building eel traps or dams to catch fish — most of which must be aimed at a Walter Mitty market of armchair survivalists.

In reality, it is highly unlikely that any survival situation is going to last more than a few days and, even if it did, only someone with the skills of a poacher or gamekeeper would be able to trap or snare a small animal to eat. Anglers and coarse fishermen would fare better if they had some crude equipment or were in the right waters at the right time of year when they might tickle a trout. But those who are ignorant of the ways of animals and fish are more likely to scare them away than to catch them. Much the easiest 'meat' to find is in grubs, worms and beetles, all high in protein and a delicacy among some primitives, as snails are to many Europeans. With wings and legs pulled off, they can be roasted over a fire or added to a vegetable soup.

Mushrooms and fungi contain protein, carbohydrates and fats, and many have a nutritional value between vegetables and meat. Of course, many are deadly and the novice would be advised to learn to recognise a few edible ones and leave everything else alone. *Food For Free* by Richard Mabey and Collins' *Guide to Mushrooms and Toadstools* are good texbooks on the subject. The inner, not the outer, bark of trees can be chewed or boiled and eaten. Hazelnuts are good food value and their shells, when ground and boiled, provide a coffee substitute. All nuts are the most concentrated of natural foods. Acorns have a bitter taste which can be leached out with water if they are first pounded or ground, and the cones of evergreens have edible nuts in them. In many areas on the coast there is an abundance of snails, limpets and mussels which can be boiled in fresh or salt water and, with a lot of luck, a crab might cling to a lure of rotten fish or meat. No seaweed is poisonous, and some is highly nutritious, but it must be fresh.

At the end of the day the most plentiful and easiest food harvest is vegetable; young ferns, for example, have edible leaves and roots. Here, in seasonal order, are some common wild foods and, if you are not a countryman, there are plenty of little pocket books with illustrations by which you will be able to recognise most of them. Berries are a risk as many of them are poisonous, so it is necessary to eat only those you know positively are edible. Grass seeds in the form of wheat, oats, rice and other cereals are the staple diet of the world. No grass seeds are poisonous and they can be gathered by winnowing — beating the heads with a stick and catching the seeds in a cloth. They can be boiled or dry roasted and pounded into meal. To heat without burning, spread them on a layer of sand over a heated surface. If you have no utensils, nothing is more useful than a sheet of kitchen foil which can be used to wrap food in for cooking in or over a fire; otherwise coat the food with mud or clay. Fish prepared with a mud coating does not need to be scaled, nor do hedgehogs need to be de-needled. The same sheet of kitchen foil can be shaped to make a crude saucepan for a brew-up or to make a vegetable soup.

EDIBLE SEAWEED

LATIN NAME	ENGLISH NAME	COLOUR	EDIBLE PARTS
Ulva lactuca	sea lettuce	green	Very common. Wash it and the entire plant can be eaten. Found both sides of the Atlantic and Pacific.
Laminaria saccfarina	sugar wrack	brown	The most common edible brown seaweed. The frond or leaf can be eaten raw when young. The young stalks are sweet to the taste. Found on both sides of the Atlantic and on the coasts of China and Japan.
Aiaria esculenta	edible kelp	brown	It should be boiled to soften it, after which it can be mixed with vegetables or soup. It is found on both sides of the Atlantic and Pacific.
Chondrus crispus	irish moss	brown	The entire plant can be eaten. Boil it into a mild drink; when mixed with milk it gives a blancmange. Found on both sides of the Atlantic and Pacific.
Porphyra	laver	shiny red or dark purple	Common and has been used as food for centuries. Still marketed in S. Wales. Clean and boil until tender (about six hours in winter and eight in summer). Mince and then fry. Found on both sides of the Atlantic and Pacific.
Rhodymenia palmata	dulse	red	Rich in protein and can be stewed to give a nutritious soup. The young fronds can be eaten raw but are tough. It is often rolled and used as a chew. It is sweet to the taste. Found on both sides of the Atlantic and in the Mediterranean.
Laminaria digitata	carweed	red	The leaf can be stewed or fried.

CALENDAR OF WILD FOODS

JANUARY-MARCH
corn salad
dandelion
herb bennet
horseradish
laurel
laver
lettuce laver (sea lettuce)
sauce-all-alone
stinging nettle (March)
tansy
watercress

APRIL-JUNE
corn salad
dandelion
elder
fairy ring mushroom
             (May-June)
fennel
field poppy (May-June)
ground elder
herb bennet
hop (May-June)
horseradish
lady's smock
laurel
nipplewort
pig nut (June)
salad burnet
samphire
sauce-all-alone
shaggy cap mushroom
             (May-June)
sorrel
sow thistle
stinging nettle (April-May)
sweet cicely (May-June)
tansy
watercress
wood sorrel

JULY-SEPTEMBER
ash (August)
barberry (Sept)
beefsteak mushroom
bilberry (Aug-Sep)
blackberry (Sep)
blewits (Sep)
corn salad
crab apple (Sep-Oct)
dandelion
elder
fairy ring mushroom
fennel
field mushroom
field poppy
ground elder
hawthorn (Sep)
hazelnuts (Sep)
herb bennet
horse mushroom
horseradish
juniper (Sep)
lady's smock
laurel
laver
nipplewort
parasol mushroom
pig nut
rose (Sep)
rowan (Aug-Sep)
salad burnet
sauce-all-alone
shaggy cap mushroom
sloe
sorrel
sow thistle
strawberry (July-Aug)
sweet cicely
tansy
watercress
wheat (Aug-Sep)

JULY-SEPTEMBER (cont'd
whortleberry (Aug-Sep)
wood sorrel
yellow goatsbeard (Sep)

OCTOBER-DECEMBER
barberry (Oct)
beech nuts (Oct-Nov)
beefsteak mushroom
             (Oct-Nov)
blewits (Oct-Nov)
corn salad
dandelion
elder (Oct)
fairy ring mushroom (Oct)
field mushroom (Oct)
hawthorn (Oct)
hazelnuts (Oct)
herb bennet
horse mushroom (Oct)
horseradish
juniper (Oct)
lady's smock (Oct)
laurel
laver
lettuce laver (sea lettuce)
parasol mushroom (Oct)
rose (Oct)
sauce-all-alone (Oct-Nov)
shaggy cap mushroom
sloe (Oct)
sweet cicely (Oct)
tansy (Oct)
watercress

Most food is more digestible if it is cooked, and cooking is the best precaution against food poisoning. But a lot of people have no idea how to make a fire, especially in damp or wet conditions. Three ingredients are needed: tinder, kindling and fuel. Good tinder is cedar bark birch bark, fine wood shavings or fettling, dry straw, sawdust, charred cloth and dry leaves. Kindling is larger material that will bring the burning point up to the temperature required to ignite larger fuel. Examples are twigs, split wood, thick cardboard and dry grass twisted into bunches. Fuel is any large form of combustible material. Matches are the best firelighters, but they need to be kept bone dry. This can be done by wrapping in polythene or keeping in a watertight container (35mm film canisters are good for this) and, as a double precaution, they can be dipped in melted candle wax. Alternatively, carry a sealed box of waterproof or lifeboat matches; it takes solid water or a hurricane to douse them. A magnifying glass works as a burning glass when there is sufficient sun; a lens screwed out of binoculars or a camera will do. Flint and steel will give sparks to ignite tinder, as will the bow and drill method. The latter is very tedious, but it does work.

Getting a fire going may need a bit of patience. First light a fistful of tinder, then transfer it to, or build over it, a pyramid of kindling, leaving plenty of air space inside. Add to the kindling as it burns, and when the flame has a good hold, start adding the larger fuel bit by bit. At this stage fires are often extinguished by squashing down the kindling with heavier fuel before it has fully caught. When a fire is needed on snow, ice or wet ground, a solid platform or hearth will be needed. This can be made of two or three layers of green logs or branches laid at right angles to each other, or built of stones; in both cases leave air space for an up-draught. These are some useful Commando hints for fire making:

Use dry wood, unless a food-smoking fire is required. Do not waste matches by trying to light a poorly prepared fire; use embers for lighting cigarettes or candles, not valuable matches; a shaved stick makes a good taper. Carry some dry tinder with you in a waterproof container, and collect kindling, tinder and other useful materials on your route — you may need them later. To keep a fire in overnight, cover the deeply glowing embers with ashes and dry earth, the embers will still be smouldering in the morning. Several small fires in a line beside you or in a circle around you will give more heat than one big one. Build up a good supply of tinder and kindling fuel before you try to light a fire as it is disheartening to have spent time lighting the tinder only to find that within minutes you have run out of fuel. A good supply of tinder must be available as a considerable amount of time may be required to nurse the fire in the early stages. When you are wet, cold and miserable, one hour spent building a shelter and a fire is worth many hours' sleep.

The contents of the survival tin, which every Commando carries, will no doubt be of interest to survival and escapist buffs, but at the same time it may provide the more down-to-earth outdoor enthusiast with some ideas of what to put into a personalised survival kit. The lid of the tin is bright and shiny so that it can act as a reflector for candlelight and also be used to signal with. The tin, if it is filled as laid down, will contain: a fluorescent red fabric marker square, a small heliograph, a magnifying/burning glass, a whistle, waterproof matches and strikers (torn off matchboxes), a capsule of lighter fuel, flint, a stub of candle, a length of fishing line, fish hooks and weights, sharp blades (razor and Stanley knife types) 3 snares, a hank of strong string or twine, a folded sheet of aluminium foil to shape into a container for boiling water and cooking food, a condom for carrying water and a hair net to carry the full condom, water purifying tablets, a 5g ($\frac{1}{5}$oz) packet of beef stock for making a hot drink, a tin opener, wire saw, a short hacksaw blade, a stub of pencil and notepad, a button compass, needle and thread, 2 safety pins, analgesic tablets, Medi Swab disinfectant wipers, suture (silk and needle), plasters, anti-diarrhoea tablets. Quite a list for so small a space. For Scotland in summer, and many other places, the addition of an insect repellent would be highly recommended.

It is included in the civilian Survival Pack sold by Survival Aids of Morland in Cumbria. Their catalogue is full of ingenious survival products for the outdoor man who has everything, but they also supply a range of first class protective clothing and camping equipment.

There is one item without which one can do very little in the way of building a shelter, harvesting food or making fires, and that is a cutting tool. An axe is ideal for felling trees. However a machete will do the same job, if less efficently, and has many other uses, performing the functions of both chopper and oversize knife. There are many so-called Commando and survival knives on the market, many of them of little use for anything but making a stealthy killing—the purpose for which they were originally designed. To be really useful in the field, a knife needs to be able to cut and chop. The best type of survival knife will have a sawback and a flat surface next to it to serve as a hammer.

In some circles the subject of survival has become somewhat distorted and made into a cult with unpleasant undertones. It does the subject no good when a publication issued by a mail order business to promote Commando daggers assures readers that: 'It has no other purpose but to kill swiftly and silently . . .', or to offer a catapult that will project a ballbearing over a quarter-mile with the tag: 'Lethal yet legal'. A pocket flare and a Mars bar would be more use to a man with a sprained ankle in the Cairngorms than a lethal catapult; a first aid kit with a good bandage would be even better.

The essentials for survival are not dangerous toys but fitness, preparedness and the will and determination to survive.

APPENDIX

The following clothing and equipment kit for beginners in outdoor activities has been compiled by the Youth Hostels Association. Prices are those prevailing in 1987. The YHA has Adventure Shops in London, Bristol, Luton, Manchester, Cambridge, Oxford, Birmingham, Cardiff and Staines. A basic kit for walkers would be:

Boots: A soft cuffed lower to middle price range pair with Vibram or Skywalk type sole such as Hawkins Glendale or High Country Dartmoor. £30-50.

Jacket: Basically any casual jacket, preferably reasonably windproof and reasonably loose fitting. In cold conditions this should be backed up with thin layers — sweaters, thermals, etc.

Trousers: Any comfortable trousers, again preferably windproof, but not jeans. In cold conditions to be backed up with thermal longjohns.

Shirt: In summer lightweight cotton; in winter wool or wool mixture.

Socks: A good wool mixture loop sock is the most comfortable. This provides cushioning for the foot as well as moisture absorption.

Compass: Nothing elaborate is required. One of the cheaper models in the Silva or Recta ranges would fill the bill — prices between £5 and £10.

Maps and Map Case: The appropriate Ordnance Survey map from the Landranger or Outdoor Leisure series is a must unless you are very familiar with your route. A clear plastic map case with neck sling will help to preserve the maps (which now cost around £3), particularly if it should rain.

Waterproofs:	These are an essential item of kit. A zip-fronted cagoule-type jacket (almost knee length) and overtrousers with zips at the bottom (so that you do not have to take off your boots to put them on) are recommended. Suitable items include Sprayway's Mountain Jacket or Craghoppers Cagjak (at around £25) and overtrousers from the same manufacturers (at around £17).
Rucksack:	A small daysack (such as Karrimor's Diddy 3 or Mountaincraft's Arran 2 or Skye 2 at around £10-12) of 20 litre capacity is ideal to carry waterproofs when not being worn, sandwiches, flask and any other bits and pieces.
Flask:	This should be of the unbreakable variety such as Camping Gaz' Bumper (at around £19.50) or one of the stainless steel kind (at around £25). Standard 'Thermos' types are not recommended as they are too fragile.

For the beginner camper/backpacker:

Tent:	A reasonable quality 2-3 man tent should be your aim. This will be comfortable for 2, palatial for 1 and acceptable for 3 for limited periods. The dome configuration gives the greatest internal volume, but a more conventional 'A' shape is also acceptable. Weight should not exceed 3·5kg so that one can carry it; if two or three are in the party each could carry a portion. Suitable domes could be Vango's Eastwind 186 or Lichfield's Sherpa, an 'A' shaped could be Lichfield's 'Mistral 2' or Viper 3 — to name but a few. Prices in the £60-100 bracket.
Rucksacks:	A good fitting internal frame of 60-65 litre capacity is the ideal. Suitable models would be Karrimor's Panther 3 or 4 (around £65), Berghaus AB60BC Lite or Laser 60 (around £80) or Mountaincraft's Super Tramper or Backpacker (around £45).
Sleeping Bag:	The requirement here depends largely on one's personal metabolism, ie if you feel the cold, and also on the times of year it is intended to be used.

For 3 season use (spring, summer, autumn —
low level — in this country) Caravan's Odin
(around £60) is to be recommended, but equally
most other bags by reputable manufacturers in a
similar price bracket (£40-60) would be suitable.
YHA's Horizon, Ultimate's Mountain King 12
or Mountain Equipment's Firebird are all good
examples. For those who do not feel the cold or
for 2 season use then a bag at between £30 and
£40 should fill the bill. Good examples of this
genre are YHA's Tramper and Super Tramper,
Caravan's Special and Snowfox and Ultimate's
Mountain King 10.

Cooking
Equipment:

This should be kept as light as possible. Gas
stoves are probably the lightest initially, but not
when you add the weight of the cartridge, and
they are certainly the slowest to cook with.
Methylated spirit burners are very light particularly as they are normally incorporated with
pan sets (such as Trangia) and are reasonably
efficient, particularly if it is windy. The most
efficient and the fastest cooking are 'petrol'
stoves — Coleman's Peak 1 and Optimus '8R'
are good examples (at around £30). Gas burners
are in the £10-15 range, and methylated spirit
stoves in the £20-25 range. Plastic crockery is
obviously ideal both from a weight and
durability standpoint.

Additional equipment:

Pocket Knife: A knife of the Swiss Army type is invaluable,
particularly one such as the Camper with its
many uses. There is a wide choice depending on
your requirements with prices ranging from £10
to £25.

Torch:

A good unbreakable torch is a must for those
jobs that may need doing in the dark. Ever
Ready's rubber torches are excellent but rather
heavy, and some of Duracell's work torches are
reasonably unbreakable in normal use.

Clothing:

A similar range of clothing to that recommended

for the walker is suitable, but spare clothing should also be carried.

For the beginner climber the best advice would be to join the local climbing club and see what the other members use, or visit the local specialist retailer who will have experienced members of staff who will make recommendations. A basic list of requirements for the rock climber should include rock boots (between £35 and £55), rope (Kernmantel by a reputable manufacturer such as Mammut or Edelrid at around £60), harness such as Troll's Freestyle or Whillans at around £25, a selection of karabiners — screwgate and snap — between £2 and £6 each, and chocks (on rope or wire) suitable for the rock type being climbed.

The mountaineer would require a similar range of hardware, but the boots must be of the Alpine variety such as Dolomite Alpiniste (£75 approx), Koflach Ultra (£115 approx). The clothing requirement for the mountaineer would normally be very different to that needed by the rock climber and specialist advice is needed here.

For those with rather more money to spend and for the more experienced Survival Aids Limited recommend the following clothing and equipment for climbers and walkers from their catalogue. They have Survival Shops at Morland in Cumbria and at Euston Station in London.

Protection:　Ventile jacket £119.95
　　　　　　 Ventile trousers £55.00
　　　　　　 Trouser belt £5.99
　　　　　　 Fibre pile jacket/jerkin £36.95/£26.95
　　　　　　 Winter shirt £24.95 or
　　　　　　 Summer bush shirt £17.95
　　　　　　 Thermal underwear £5.95-£19.95
　　　　　　 Explorer socks £5.95
　　　　　　 Lundhag boots £69-£89
　　　　　　 Silk thermals £19.95
　　　　　　 Taped survival blanket £2.95
　　　　　　 Double hooped bivi £117 or
　　　　　　 Solus bivi tent £169.95
　　　　　　 Allweather outer sleeping bag £54.95
　　　　　　 Allweather inner £45.95
　　　　　　 Explorer or down inner £45.95/£89.95

Meraklon liner £17.95
Kip mat £7.95
Repel 100 (insect repellent) £2.95
Zip-O-Gage (thermometer & wind chill gauge) £2.95
Individual first aid kit £7.95

Location: Mini Flare Mk III £14.95
SA24 compass £13.95
Mini binoculars £64.95
Map case £12.95
Map measurer £8.95
Tekna torch £5.95-£19.95

Water/Food: Survival straw £5.95
Aquafilta £12.95
Purification tablets £1.10
Emergency rations £5.95
Trangia 27 or Peak One Stove £21.95/£32.95
Knife, fork, spoon set £3.95

Tools: Walkers Go Pack (very basic survival kit) £6.95
Zippo or Remington lighter £9.95/£14.95
Lifeboat matches 75p
Pocket knife £13.95
Camera pouch £21.95
Compass pouch £2.95
Neck or belt pouch £5.95/£3.95
Cyclops Roc bergen £82.95 (70 litre)
Crusader bergen £139.95 (100 litre)
Waterproof notebook £2.85
Paracord £2.50
Bungees (shock cords) £4.95
Field towel(s) £2.95/£6.95 pack of 3

Items popular with military personnel:

Protection: DPM Ventile jacket £99
and trousers £59.95
SAS Smock/trousers £79.95/£49.95
Gore-Tex Lionheart jacket/overtrousers £109.95/£64.95
Fibre pile jacket/jerkin £36.95/£26.95 or
Woolly Pully £29.95

Norwegian army shirt (winter) £16.95 or
OG shirt (summer) £17.95
DPM Scrim scarf £3.95
Thermal clothing £3.95-£15.95
Arctic/Explorer socks £4.95/£5.95
Diagonal zip bivi bag £84.95
DPM or Green double hooped bivi £117
DPM or Green allweather outer and inner
  £54.95/£45.95
Meraklon liner £17.95
Kip mat £7.95
Bollé Commander (sunglasses) £19.95
Repel 100 £2.95
Mosquito net £26.95
Bivi boots £19.95

Location:　　SA24 Compass
Mini binoculars £64.95
DPM Map case £12.95
Map measurer £8.95
Casio DW5200C (water-resistant watch)
  £39.95
Tekna torch £19.95-£21.95

Water/Food:　'85 Pattern water battle mug £9.95
Survival straw £5.95
Mini cooker and refills (refills) £1.25
Mess tin lid £6.95

Tools:　　　Combat survival kit £16.95
Zippo or Remington lighter £9.95/£14.95
Lifeboat matches 75p
Mauser Officer's pocket knife £13.95
MOD survival knife £29.95
Quick release belt £9.95
Roll pin belt £9.95
SAS webbing set £13 approx
DPM Crusader bergen £139.95
DPM bergen cover £9.95
Waterproof notebook £2.85
Paracord £2.50
Bungees £4.95
Field towel(s) £2.95/£6.95 (pack of 3)

INDEX